Synthesis of Optimum Nonlinear Control Systems

M.I.T. PRESS RESEARCH MONOGRAPHS

SYNTHESIS OF OPTIMUM NONLINEAR CONTROL SYSTEMS
By Harry L. Van Trees

DYNAMIC OPTIMIZATION AND CONTROL: A VARIATIONAL APPROACH
By Walerian Kipiniak

ITERATIVE ARRAYS OF LOGICAL CIRCUITS
By Frederick C. Hennie III

SEQUENTIAL DECODING
By John M. Wozencraft and Barney Reiffen

THE CONTROL OF MULTIVARIABLE SYSTEMS
By Mihajlo D. Mesarović

FREQUENCY-POWER FORMULAS
By Paul Penfield, Jr.

ELECTRONIC PROCESSING IN SOLIDS
By Pierre R. Aigrain

THE DYNAMIC BEHAVIOR OF THERMOELECTRIC DEVICES
By Paul E. Gray

HYDROMAGNETIC CHANNEL FLOWS
By Lawson P. Harris

PROCESSING NEUROELECTRIC DATA
By Walter A. Rosenblith and Members of the Communications Biophysics Group

MATHEMATICAL PROGRAMMING AND ELECTRICAL NETWORKS
By Jack B. Dennis

CIRCUIT THEORY OF LINEAR NOISY NETWORKS
By Hermann A. Haus and Richard B. Adler

NONLINEAR PROBLEMS IN RANDOM THEORY
By Norbert Wiener

by

HARRY L. VAN TREES

Assistant Professor of Electrical Engineering
Massachusetts Institute of Technology

Synthesis of Optimum Nonlinear Control Systems

The M.I.T. Press

Massachusetts Institute of Technology
Cambridge, Massachusetts
1962

Library of Congress Catalog Card Number: 62-19757

Printed in the United States of America

FOREWORD

There has long been a need in science and engineering for systematic publication of research studies larger in scope than a journal article but less ambitious than a finished book. Much valuable work of this kind is now published only in a semiprivate way, perhaps as a laboratory report, and so may not find its proper place in the literature of the field. The present contribution is the thirteenth of the M. I. T. Press Research Monographs, which we hope will make selected timely research studies readily accessible to libraries and to the independent worker.

J. A. Stratton

ACKNOWLEDGMENT

This is Special Technical Report Number 5 of the Research Laboratory of Electronics of the Massachusetts Institute of Technology.

The Research Laboratory of Electronics is an interdepartmental laboratory in which faculty members and graduate students from numerous academic departments conduct research.

The research reported in this document was made possible in part by support extended the Massachusetts Institute of Technology, Research Laboratory of Electronics, jointly by the U.S. Army (Signal Corps), the U.S. Navy (Office of Naval Research), and the U.S. Air Force (Office of Scientific Research) under Signal Corps Contract DA 36-039-sc-78108, Department of the Army Task 3-99-20-001 and Project 3-99-00-000; and in part by Signal Corps Contract DA-SIG-36-039-61-G14.

PREFACE

In linear systems, it is meaningful to talk about what is the "best" analysis or synthesis technique because all linear systems have the property of superposition as a common basis. By contrast, nonlinear systems have no simple unifying property. One would indeed be optimistic to hope for an analysis or synthesis technique that would be best in all cases. Thus, one is faced with two alternatives. The first possibility is to pick a specific nonlinear device and devote one's effort to the detailed analysis of it. In general, the techniques one develops will not be easily adaptable to another nonlinear system. The second approach is to concentrate on techniques which are not oriented toward a specific system. In this approach, one attempts to make the class of systems to which the method applies as large as possible. Clearly, in a specific problem, the general approach might be much more involved than a technique designed for that specific problem. In this book we shall use the second approach.

In Chapter 1, the philosophy behind our synthesis approach is outlined. In Chapter 2, we develop the mathematical techniques that we shall need in the sequel. Chapters 3 and 4 present two alternative methods of synthesizing a desired control system. For the techniques in Chapters 3 and 4 to be applicable, the fixed elements in the system must be controllable. Chapter 5 deals with the determination of the controllability of the fixed elements. Chapter 6 discusses the limitations of the work and possible extensions.

There exists a large class of control systems to which the technique developed here is applicable. The obvious disadvantage is the resulting complexity. It is felt that in some cases the complexity is warranted. In other cases, the optimum solution will provide a standard of comparison for simpler, but less efficient, systems. In either case, one gains insight into the difficult problem of nonlinear synthesis.

The research reported in this book was conducted while the author was a member of the Statistical Communication Theory Group of the Research Laboratory of Electronics at the Massachusetts Institute of Technology. It is essentially the same as a doctoral thesis submitted to the Department of Electrical Engineering in May, 1961. The thesis was supervised by Professor Y. W. Lee, who provided a constant source of encouragement. Professors Samuel J. Mason and A. G. Bose were members of the thesis committee.

During the years 1959-1961, the period when this research was conducted, the author was supported by the National Science Foundation on a Fellowship.

Cambridge, Massachusetts
June 18, 1962

Harry L. Van Trees

CONTENTS

Chapter 1

THE NONLINEAR CONTROL PROBLEM

In a typical communications system problem there is a message available which has been corrupted by noise. After we specify the purpose of the system, we attempt to process the input in some optimum fashion to achieve this purpose. For instance, we may merely want to know if a signal is present. We then have a detection problem. A second case is when the message consists of a sequence of finite-time signals from a fixed set available at the transmitter. We wish to decide which of the signals is present during each time interval. We then are faced with a decision problem. A third case is when the message is a sample function from a random process. The goal of the receiving system is to provide an accurate reproduction of message. This third case, the filtering problem, will be of principal interest to us.

In order to solve the filtering problem analytically, several conditions must be specified. We must include:

(1) An error criterion.
(2) The amount of past history of the input that is available for processing.
(3) The class of allowable systems.

The error criterion provides a quantitative measure of the accuracy of our reproduction of the message. If the desired output is $f_d(t)$ and the actual output is $f_o(t)$, a useful error criterion is the mean-square error criterion:

$$\overline{E^2} = \lim_{T\to\infty} \frac{1}{2T} \int_{-T}^{T} [f_d(t) - f_o(t)]^2 \, dt \tag{1.1}$$

We shall assume that the infinite past of the input is available for processing. In general, the optimum filter uses the distant past very little, so that our assumption is valid.

In the original work in the field, Wiener[30] considered the class of realizable, linear systems. For this class of inputs, he obtained a closed-form solution for the optimum linear system. This original work and later developments are covered by Lee[15]. We shall assume that the reader is familiar with the latter reference.

Clearly, the optimum linear filter is not always the best solution to a particular problem. As a simple example, consider the case where the message and noise spectra are identical.

In the following instance, the power density spectrum of the message, $\Phi_{mm}(\omega)$, is

$$\Phi_{mm}(\omega) = \frac{1}{2\pi} \frac{8}{1 + \omega^2} \tag{1.2}$$

The power density spectrum of the noise, $\Phi_{nn}(\omega)$, is

$$\Phi_{nn}(\omega) = \frac{1}{2\pi} \frac{1}{1 + \omega^2} \tag{1.3}$$

The message and noise are sample functions from independent random processes.

The optimum linear filter is simply an attenuator with gain $K = 8/9$, and the resulting mean-square error is 4/9. This follows since the optimum linear filtering solution uses only spectral information.

If, in addition, one knew the first-order probability density of message and noise, it might be possible to design a nonlinear filter to obtain a smaller mean-square error. For example, let the first-order probability density of the message ensemble be

$$P_{\xi}(x) = \frac{1}{2} [u_0(x + 2) + u_0(x - 2)] \tag{1.4}$$

where $u_0(x)$ is a unit impulse function at $x = 0$, and for the noise ensemble,

$$P_{\eta}(y) = \frac{1}{2} \left[u_0\left(y + \frac{1}{\sqrt{2}}\right) + u_0\left(y - \frac{1}{\sqrt{2}}\right)\right] \tag{1.5}$$

Clearly, a symmetric limiter with two possible outputs, +2 and -2, would provide an optimum nonlinear filter with zero mean-square error. Unfortunately, except for a few simple cases, the calculation of the optimum nonlinear filter is difficult.

Often, however, the reduction in error obtained justifies the additional complexity of a nonlinear system. It is with such cases that we are concerned.

1. The Relation between Communication and Control Systems

Communication systems and control systems have much in common. In a control system, we have available an input signal. We want the output of some physical device (fixed elements) to follow this signal. The simplest way to do this is to operate on the system input to obtain an input to the fixed elements that will cause the desired output. The block diagram of a cascade system is shown in Figure 1.1. In practice, one generally employs a feedback control system, as shown in Figure 1.2. The control problem reduces to finding a suitable compensation scheme.

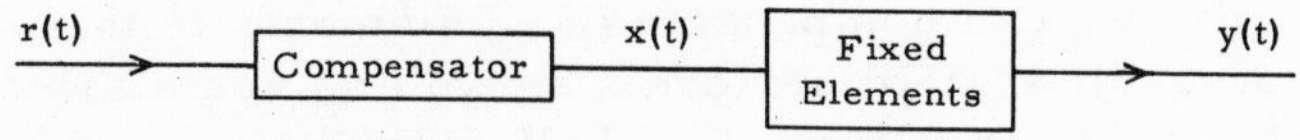

Figure 1.1. Cascade compensation

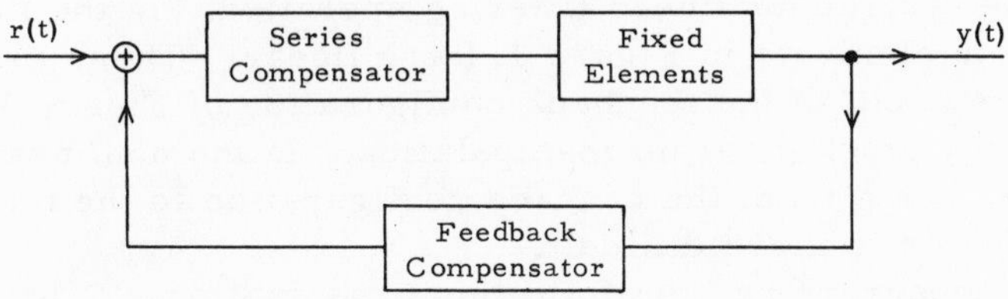

Figure 1.2. Closed-loop compensation

There are two cases of interest. When noise is unimportant, one designs the compensator so that the over-all system will exhibit satisfactory dynamic behavior. Most of the earlier work in the control field[6] considered this problem.

The case of interest to us is when the input consists of some desired signal, the message, corrupted by noise. We want to synthesize a compensator so that the output of the fixed elements will accurately reproduce the message. More generally, we may want to produce some function of the message (e.g., prediction, differentiation). In this instance, the control problem becomes essentially a signal-processing problem. The basic difference is the presence of fixed elements in the configuration. Our approach to the control problem is to view it as a filtering problem with a constraint.

For linear systems with random or deterministic inputs, the relation between the two problems is well known. The solution for the optimum linear filter leads directly to the optimum compensator. If the fixed elements are minimum-phase, the optimum linear control system performs as well as the optimum linear filter. In this case, the compensation device essentially removes the effect of the fixed elements. If the fixed elements are nonminimum-phase, an explicit solution for the optimum compensator is available.

For nonlinear systems the relation between the filtering

problem and the control problem is not yet clear. The object of this research is to develop an approach to the nonlinear compensation problem which is based on the corresponding nonlinear filter problem. Our development will be somewhat analogous to the linear compensation problem.

First, we shall define a class of fixed elements which do not impose a performance restriction on the over-all system. In other words, we can compensate fixed elements in this class so that the over-all system performs as well as some arbitrary realizable nonlinear filter. We shall describe these fixed elements as completely controllable. Sufficiency tests to determine inclusion in this class are shown.

Secondly, we must develop a closed-loop configuration that gives the desired nonlinear filtering operation. In the linear case, both elements in Figure 1.1 are linear. Thus, to synthesize the system in the feedback configuration of Figure 1.2 requires only block diagram manipulation. In the nonlinear case, however, going from the cascade configuration to the feedback configuration is more difficult.

This monograph has the following organization. First, the general problem and our specific approach are outlined. Before discussing the solution, previous related work is briefly reviewed.

Next, the problem of characterization is considered. In our approach two methods of characterization are used. The fixed elements will be described by a nonlinear differential equation. The over-all system and the compensation devices will be described by a functional expansion of the Volterra type. In Chapter 2, we discuss the functional method of characterizing nonlinear systems. Properties analogous to real part sufficiency and gain-minimum-phase relations will be derived. Necessary and sufficient conditions for an nth-order kernel to represent a stable system are shown.

In Chapter 3, we combine the differential equation representation and the functional representation in order to develop an algorithm that gives the form of the desired compensator. The compensator consists of combinations of various higher-order kernels. In general, our solution will only converge over some finite range of inputs. To avoid convergence problems, an alternative approach is developed in Chapter 4 which always leads to a closed-form solution.

Implicit in both of these methods is the assumption that the fixed elements are controllable. In Chapter 5, sufficiency tests to determine controllability are shown.

Finally, in Chapter 6, some of the ramifications of the solution and possible extensions are discussed.

2. An Approach to the Nonlinear Compensation Problem

The general configuration of a feedback control system is shown in Figure 1.2. In general, r(t) is a sample function from an ergodic random process. The following techniques could be applied equally well, however, to deterministic inputs. The desired output of the over-all system is a function $y_d(t)$ which is related to either r(t) or the signal part of r(t) in some known manner. If there were no fixed elements, we would have the nonlinear filter problem illustrated in Figure 1.3.

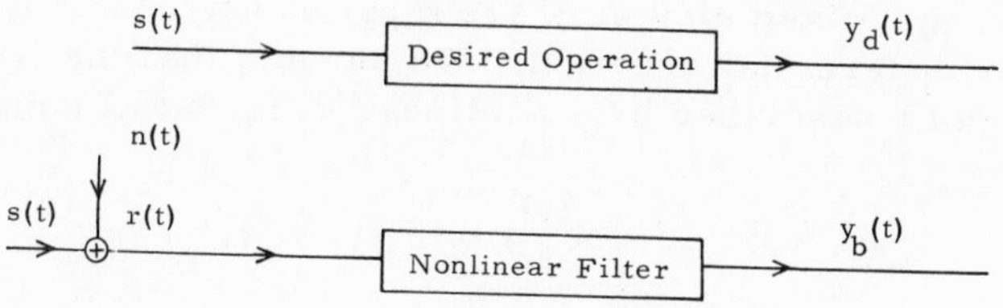

Figure 1.3. Optimum filter problem

One method of solving this filter problem would be to specify the input-output relation of the filter in some time-invariant functional form. For example,

$$y_b(t) = F[r(t_1;\ t_1 \leq t)] \tag{1.6}$$

Here $y_b(t)$ depends on the past of the input r(t).

Using a mean-square error criterion, the filter error is

$$\overline{E_f^2} = \lim_{T\to\infty} \frac{1}{2T}\int_{-T}^{T} [y_d(t) - y_b(t)]^2\, dt \tag{1.7}$$

$$\overline{E_f^2} = \overline{[y_d(t) - F[r(t_1;\ t_1 \leq t)]]^2} \tag{1.8}$$

Now one finds the functional F that causes $\overline{E^2}$ to be a minimum. For the present, we shall assume that we have this functional available. Techniques for finding F are discussed by Wiener,[31] Bose,[4] and Chesler.[8]

Using the solution to the related filtering problem, we want to find a realizable system C_a or C_b such that $y(t) = y_b(t)$. In practice, the filter functional belongs to some class of nonlinear functionals. As this class becomes more inclusive, our approach is equivalent to minimizing the control system error directly:

$$\overline{E_c^2} = \overline{[y_d(t) - y(t)]^2} = \overline{E_f^2} \qquad y(t) = y_b(t) \tag{1.9}$$

Thus our approach consists of specifying F and then finding a realizable compensator so that the closed-loop system of Figure 1.2 duplicates this functional.

To proceed, we must have a suitable way to characterize the input-output relations of both the fixed elements and the compensation devices.

In practice, fixed elements are most easily described by a nonlinear differential equation. We assume that the fixed elements can be described by a nonlinear differential equation of the form

$$P_1(x, \dot{x}, \ddot{x}, \ldots, x^{(r)}) = P_2(y, \dot{y}, \ddot{y}, \ldots, y^{(s)}) \tag{1.10}$$

where x is the input to the fixed elements, y is the output of the fixed elements, and P represents a function that is a polynomial. Typical examples of the occurrence of equations of this type are

$$a\ddot{y} + b\dot{y} + cy + dy^3 = x \tag{1.11}$$

which represents motion with nonlinear restoring force;

$$a\ddot{y} + b(\dot{y})^2 + cy = x \tag{1.12}$$

which represents motion with nonlinear damping; and

$$a\ddot{y} + b\dot{y} + cy = P(x) \tag{1.13}$$

which represents the general class of systems which are a cascade of a nonlinear no-memory polynomial device and a linear memory device.

More general polynomials such as

$$a\ddot{y}y + b(\dot{y})^3 + cy^2 = dx + e\ddot{x}\dot{x} + fx^3 \tag{1.14}$$

are included in this class.

From the Weierstrass theorem, we know that any nonlinear device whose output is a continuous function of all of the input-state variables $(x, \dot{x}, \ddot{x}, \ldots, x^{(r)})$ can be approximated arbitrarily closely over a finite range of these input-state variables by a polynomial. Thus our model of the fixed elements is fairly general. The classical study of nonlinear physical systems has been devoted to the properties of nonlinear differential equations. Minorsky[22] has summarized the earlier work. Expositions of more recent work have been given by Leimanis and Minorsky[16] and by Nemytskii and Stetpanov.[23] Analytical work along these classical lines has dealt primarily with the properties of solutions to homogeneous differential equations and systems with deterministic inputs. An obvious disadvantage of a differential equation characterization is that the input-output relation is implicit.

The method of characterizing the compensation devices is related to the form of the functional F. We shall express the functional F and the compensation devices by use of a functional power series of the Volterra type. This method of characterization and its properties are discussed in Chapter 2. We shall see that an obvious advantage is that the output is expressed as an explicit functional of the input.

Chapter 2

NONLINEAR SYSTEM CHARACTERIZATION

1. The Functional Representation

In a linear system, one uses the convolution integral as a convenient functional to describe the input-output relation. Thus, for a system with an impulse response h(t) and an input x(t), the output y(t) is expressed as

$$y(t) = \int_{-\infty}^{\infty} h(\tau)\, x(t-\tau)\, d\tau = \int_{-\infty}^{\infty} h(t-\tau)\, x(\tau)\, d\tau \quad (2.1)$$

The simple RC filter in Figure 2.1 has an impulse response $h(t) = u_{-1}(t)\, \alpha e^{-\alpha t}$.

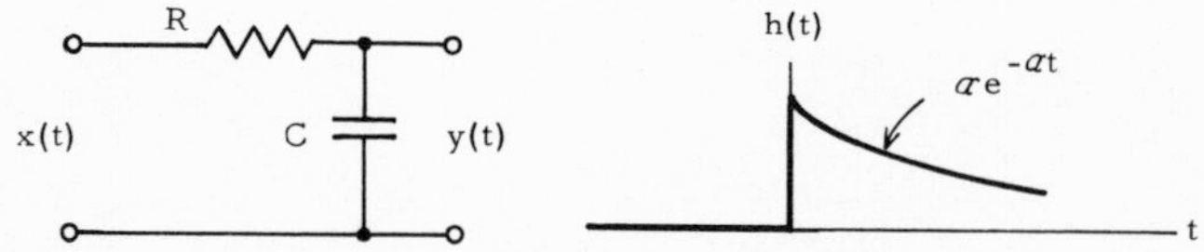

Figure 2. 1. Simple RC filter

The impulse response is simply the solution to the system differential equation

$$\frac{dy}{dt} + \alpha y = \alpha x \quad (2.2)$$

when $x(t) = u_0(t)$, the unit impulse function.

A system impulse response is realizable if it is zero for $t < 0$.

An example of an impulse response corresponding to a nonrealizable system is shown in Figure 2. 2a. It is nonrealizable because the output occurs before the input.

A system impulse response is stable if the integral

$$\int_{-\infty}^{\infty} |h(t)|\, dt < \infty$$

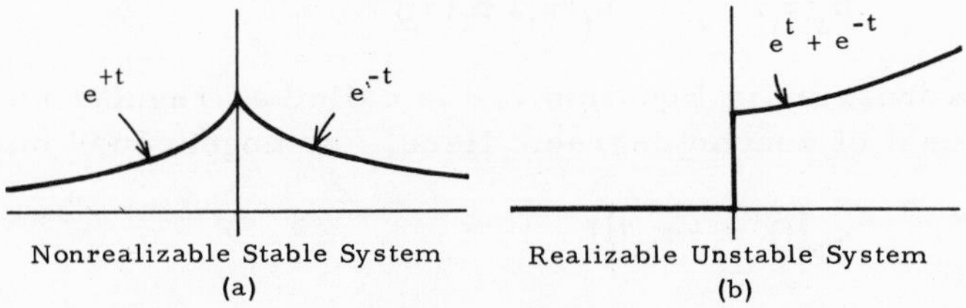

Figure 2. 2. Typical impulse responses

This is equivalent to saying that any bounded input to the system will cause a bounded output. An impulse response corresponding to an unstable linear system is shown in Figure 2. 2b.

Now consider a simple nonlinear system formed by cascading the RC filter with a square-law device, as shown in Figure 2. 3.

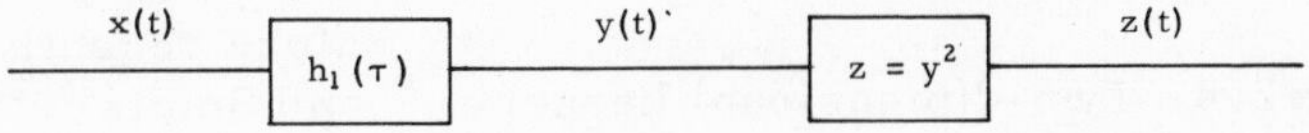

Figure 2. 3. Simple nonlinear system

Since

$$y(t) = \int_{-\infty}^{\infty} h(\tau)\, x(t - \tau)\, d\tau \tag{2.3}$$

and

$$z(t) = y^2(t) \tag{2.4}$$

we can write

$$z(t) = \int_{-\infty}^{\infty} h(\tau_1)\, x(t - \tau_1)\, d\tau_1 \int_{-\infty}^{\infty} h(\tau_2)\, x(t - \tau_2)\, d\tau_2 \tag{2.5}$$

or

$$z(t) = \int_{-\infty}^{\infty}\int_{-\infty}^{\infty} h_1(\tau_1)\, h_1(\tau_2)\, x(t - \tau_1)\, x(t - \tau_2)\, d\tau_1\, d\tau_2$$

$$= \int_{-\infty}^{\infty}\int_{-\infty}^{\infty} h_2(\tau_1, \tau_2)\, x(t - \tau_1)\, x(t - \tau_2)\, d\tau_1\, d\tau_2 \tag{2.6}$$

Therefore the operation of the over-all system could be expressed compactly by a double convolution of the input x(t) and a two-dimensional kernel $h_2(\tau_1, \tau_2)$. Here $h_2(\tau_1, \tau_2)$ is defined as

$$h_2(\tau_1, \tau_2) \equiv h_1(\tau_1)\, h_1(\tau_2) \qquad (2.7)$$

The expression in Equation 2.6 is called a "regular homogeneous" functional of second degree. Here, "homogeneous" means that if

$$x_\beta(t) = k x_\alpha(t) \qquad (2.8)$$

then the resulting output

$$z_\beta(t) = k^2 z_\alpha(t) \qquad (2.9)$$

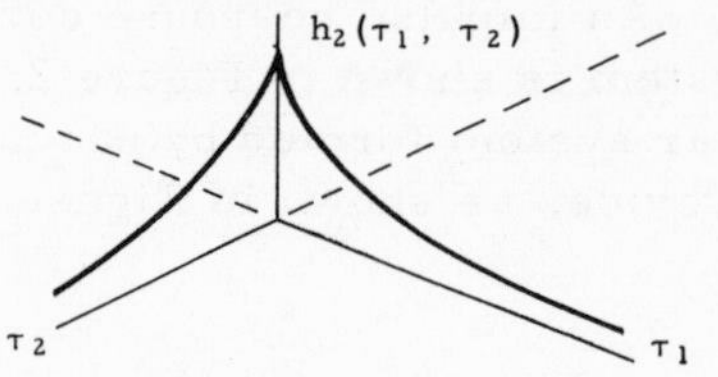

Figure 2.4. Two-dimensional kernel

Functionals of this type were introduced and extensively studied by Volterra.[29] The first application to nonlinear systems analysis was by Wiener.[2] More recently, Barrett and Smets[26,27] have applied them to practical problems.

Figure 2.4 is a sketch of the two-dimensional kernel. Just as in the linear case, we call a kernel "realizable" if

$$h_2(\tau_1, \tau_2) = 0 \qquad \text{for either } \tau_1 \text{ or } \tau_2 < 0 \qquad (2.10)$$

and "stable" if

$$\int_{-\infty}^{\infty}\int_{-\infty}^{\infty} |h_2(\tau_1, \tau_2)|\, d\tau_1\, d\tau_2 < \infty \qquad (2.11)$$

Volterra restricted his work to functionals with realizable kernels. Thus a Volterra kernel is, by definition, a realizable kernel.

The second-degree functional has several obvious advantages. Since the input-output relation is explicit, the output for periodic or transient inputs is obtained by a straightforward double convolution. Similarly, the moments of the output z(t) may be found as in the linear case. Thus when x(t) is a member function from a stationary random process, the mean of z(t) is

$$\overline{z(t)} = \int_{-\infty}^{\infty}\int_{-\infty}^{\infty} h_2(\tau_1, \tau_2)\, \overline{x(t-\tau_1)\, x(t-\tau_2)}\, d\tau_1\, d\tau_2$$

$$= \int_{-\infty}^{\infty}\int_{-\infty}^{\infty} h_2(\tau_1, \tau_2)\, \phi_{xx}(\tau_1 - \tau_2)\, d\tau_1\, d\tau_2 \qquad (2.12)$$

where $\phi_{xx}(\tau)$ is the autocorrelation function of the input process. The autocorrelation function of z(t) and other higher-order moments follow in a similar manner. One may observe that to find an nth-order moment of the output of a second-order system we require the input correlation function of order 2n.

The particular kernel we have constructed is "separable." In other words, $h_2(\tau_1, \tau_2)$ can be factored in a product of a function of τ_1 only and a function of τ_2 only. Thus

$$h_2(\tau_1, \tau_2) = h_1(\tau_1)\, h_1(\tau_2) \tag{2.13}$$

Clearly, all second-order kernels are not separable. An easy counterexample is found by connecting two systems in parallel. Each system has the form of the system in Figure 2.3. The time constant of the RC filters, however, is different. The resulting system is shown in Figure 2.5.

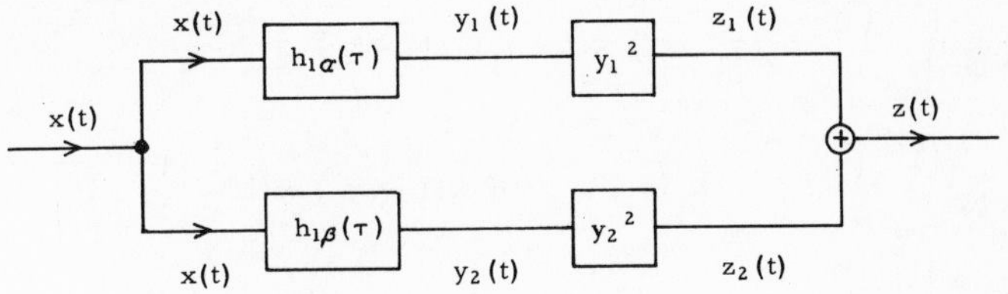

Figure 2.5. System with nonseparable kernel

Since $z(t) = z_1(t) + z_2(t)$, the functional relation follows directly from Equation 2.5, and

$$z(t) = \int_{-\infty}^{\infty}\int_{-\infty}^{\infty} \left[h_{1\alpha}(\tau_1)\, h_{1\alpha}(\tau_2) + h_{1\beta}(\tau_1)\, h_{1\beta}(\tau_2)\right] x(t-\tau_1)\, x(t-\tau_2)\, d\tau_1\, d\tau_2 \tag{2.14}$$

The resultant second-degree kernel is

$$h_2(\tau_1, \tau_2) = h_{1\alpha}(\tau_1)\, h_{1\alpha}(\tau_2) + h_{1\beta}(\tau_1)\, h_{1\beta}(\tau_2) \tag{2.15}$$

This kernel does not factor unless $h_{1\alpha}(\tau) = h_{1\beta}(\tau)$. Thus, for a simple nonlinear system, we have a simple functional representation which has many desirable properties.

Now replace the square-law device in Figure 2.3 with an arbitrary continuous function. In other words, the instantaneous value of z(t) is determined from the instantaneous value of y(t) by the relation

$$z(t) = f[y(t)] \tag{2.16}$$

If x(t) is bounded and $h_1(\tau)$ is stable, then y(t) will also be bounded. Since

$$|y(t)| = \left| \int_{-\infty}^{\infty} h(\tau)\, x(t-\tau)\, d\tau \right| \leq \int_{-\infty}^{\infty} |h(\tau)|\, d\tau \cdot |x(t)| \qquad (2.17)$$

From the Weierstrass theorem we know that there exists a sequence of polynomials that converge everywhere to f(y). For bounded functions, this implies convergence in the mean. Thus we can approximate f(y) by $f_N(y)$:

$$f_N(y) = a_{0N} + a_{1N}\, y + a_{2N}\, y^2 + a_{3N}\, y^3 + \ldots + a_{NN}\, y^N \qquad (2.18)$$

Now we can represent this approximate system by a sum of regular homogeneous functionals of degree $\leq N$. Using reasoning analogous to the second-order case, we have

$$\begin{aligned} z_N(t) &= a_{0N} + a_{1N} \int_{-\infty}^{\infty} h_1(\tau)\, x(t-\tau)\, d\tau \\ &+ a_{2N} \int_{-\infty}^{\infty}\int_{-\infty}^{\infty} h_2(\tau_1, \tau_2)\, x(t-\tau_1)\, x(t-\tau_2)\, d\tau_1 d\tau_2 \\ &+ a_{3N} \int_{-\infty}^{\infty}\int_{-\infty}^{\infty}\int_{-\infty}^{\infty} h_3(\tau_1, \tau_2, \tau_3)\, x(t-\tau_1)\, x(t-\tau_2)\, x(t-\tau_3)\, d\tau_1\, d\tau_2\, d\tau_3 \\ &+ \ldots \\ &+ a_{NN} \int_{-\infty}^{\infty} \cdots \int_{-\infty}^{\infty} h_N(\tau_1, \ldots, \tau_N)\, x(t-\tau_1) \ldots x(t-\tau_N)\, d\tau_1 \ldots d\tau_N \end{aligned} \qquad (2.19)$$

where

$$h_3(\tau_1, \tau_2, \tau_3) = h_1(\tau_1)\, h_1(\tau_2)\, h_1(\tau_3) \qquad (2.20)$$

and

$$h_N(\tau_1, \ldots, \tau_N) = h_1(\tau_1) \cdot h_1(\tau_2) \ldots h_1(\tau_N) \qquad (2.21)$$

As we increase the accuracy of our approximation to f(y), our functional representation more accurately approximates the actual system.

Alternately, if f(y) is analytic in some region, one could expand it in a power series:

$$z(t) = f[y(t)] = b_0 + b_1 y + b_2 y^2 + \ldots \qquad (2.22)$$

The advantage of the power series is that one can determine a bound on the error. The disadvantage is the restricted region of validity.

This power series will converge for all $|y(t)| < \epsilon$. The system peration could be represented by a "functional power series":

$$y(t) = \sum_{n=0}^{\infty} b_n \int_{-\infty}^{\infty} \ldots \int_{-\infty}^{\infty} h_n(\tau_1, \ldots, \tau_n)\, x(t-\tau_1) \ldots x(t-\tau_n)\, d\tau_1 \ldots, d\tau_n \tag{2.23}$$

As above, each kernel $h_n(\tau_1, \ldots, \tau_n)$ is separable. Using this eparability and Equation 2.19, we see that the functional power eries will converge for all

$$|x(t)| < \frac{\epsilon}{\int_{-\infty}^{\infty} |h(\tau)|\, d\tau} \tag{2.24}$$

In the region of convergence of the functional power series, e two representations are the same in the limit. Nonlinear ystems which may be represented by a functional power series ith a nonzero radius of convergence are called "analytic systems." nalytic systems have been discussed in detail by Brilliant.[5]

In this simple cascade case, the construction of the functional epresentation is straightforward. One could construct more omplicated systems by alternating linear and nonlinear no- emory devices in arbitrarily long cascades. A large number practical nonlinear systems fall into this category.

In the optimization problem, we are going to find the filter hich minimizes the mean-square error. Initially, we must oose a method of characterizing a class of nonlinear systems. hen the nonlinear filter of this class which gives the smallest ean-square error is selected as the optimum filter. In general,† the class of available systems becomes more inclusive, the esultant error decreases. Therefore we are concerned with e generality of the class of nonlinear systems which we can epresent using a functional expansion.

Generality of Functional Representation

Fréchet[10] showed that for any continuous functional

$$y(t_1) = F[r(t;\ a < t < t_1)] \tag{2.25}$$

ere exists a sequence of functionals which approximate $[r(t;\ a < t < t_1)]$ arbitrarily closely in the limit.

In a continuous functional, two input functions which are close" to each other give rise to two values of the functional hich are close.

A well-known exception is the case of a desired linear operation a Gaussian process. Here the class of linear system is ade- ate to give the minimum mean-square error.

Now in the case of functions, the Weierstrass theorem guarantees the existence of a convergent sequence but does not show how to find it. In practice, to approximate a continuous function, one uses a set of orthogonal polynomials. Similarly, Fréchet guarantees the existence of a sequence of functionals but does not show how to find them. Thus an orthogonal development for a nonlinear functional is necessary.

Cameron and Martin[7] consider functionals whose values depend on the values of a real function over a finite interval. These functions are continuous and square-integrable over this interval. They show that these functionals can be represented as a cascade of two operations. The first operation uses a complete set of functions which are orthonormal over the finite interval. The input function x(t) and each function of the set are averaged over the interval to give a set of numbers

$$x_p = \int_0^1 x(t)\, \alpha_p(t)\, dt \qquad p = 1, 2, 3, \ldots \tag{2.26}$$

where $\alpha_p(t)$ are the functions of the orthonormal set. The second operation uses the set of Hermite polynomials

$$H_n(u) = (-1)^n\, 2^{-\frac{n}{2}}\, (n!)^{-\frac{1}{2}}\, e^{u^2} \frac{d^n}{du^n} (e^{-u^2}) \qquad n = 0, 1, \ldots \tag{2.27}$$

They then define

$$\Phi_{m,p}(x) \equiv H_m[x_p] = H_m\left[\int_0^1 x(t)\, \alpha_p(t)\, dt\right] \qquad \begin{cases} m = 0, 1, 2, \ldots \\ p = 1, 2, \ldots \end{cases} \tag{2.28}$$

and

$$\Psi_{m_1, \ldots, m_p}(x) = \Phi_{m_1, 1}(x) \ldots \Phi_{m_p, p} \tag{2.29}$$

where $m_1, \ldots, m_p$ may be any nonnegative integers.

In other words, the $\Phi_{m,p}(x)$ are formed by operating on the x_p with the various Hermite polynomials. The outputs of these operations are multiplied together in all possible ways.

Finally, a weighted sum of the $\Psi_{m_1, \ldots, m_N}$ is formed. It is shown that this sum

$$\sum_{m_1, \ldots, m_N = 0}^{N} A_{m_1}, \ldots, A_{m_N} \Psi_{m_1, \ldots, m_N}(x)$$

converges to F[x] as $N \to \infty$.

The restriction to functions over a finite interval excludes a number of useful systems. The simplest example is the RC filter whose output at time t = 0 depends on the infinite past.

Wiener[31]† considers the class of nonlinear systems whose output depends to an arbitrarily small extent on the remote past. He shows that this class of nonlinear systems can be represented by a cascade of two operations.

The first operation uses a set of Laguerre functions. These functions are orthonormal over a semi-infinite interval. The output of this first operation is a set of numbers:

$$x_p = \int_{-\infty}^{0} x(t)\, \ell_p(-t)\, dt \tag{2.30}$$

The second operation uses the set of Hermite polynomials H_n operating on the various x_p to give $H_n(x_p)$. The $\Psi(x)$ are formed as above. Finally, a weighted sum of the $\Psi(x)$ gives the output.

Physically, the first operation in Figure 2.6 is performed by a set of Laguerre networks. These are linear systems whose impulse responses are[15]

$$\ell_n(\tau) = e^{-\frac{\tau}{2}} \left\{ \frac{1}{(n-1)!}\, e^{\tau} \frac{d^{(n-1)}}{d\tau^{(n-1)}} \left(\tau^{n-1} e^{-\tau}\right) \right\} \quad \text{for } \tau \geq 0 \tag{2.31}$$

Using the convolution integral, we see that the output of kth network at t = 0 is

$$x_k = \int_{-\infty}^{0} x(\tau)\, \ell_k(-\tau)\, d\tau \tag{2.32}$$

Thus the output of this set of Laguerre networks is a set of numbers which characterize the past of the input.

The first few Hermite polynomials are

$$H_0(x) = 1$$

$$H_1(x) = x$$

$$H_2(x) = x^2 - 1$$

$$H_3(x) = x^3 - 3x$$

A representative section of the system in Figure 2.6a is shown in Figure 2.6b. Now we can rearrange the no-memory box by collecting terms of a similar nature. A typical section of the resulting system is shown in Figure 2.7.

---

† This subject is also discussed by Bose.[4]

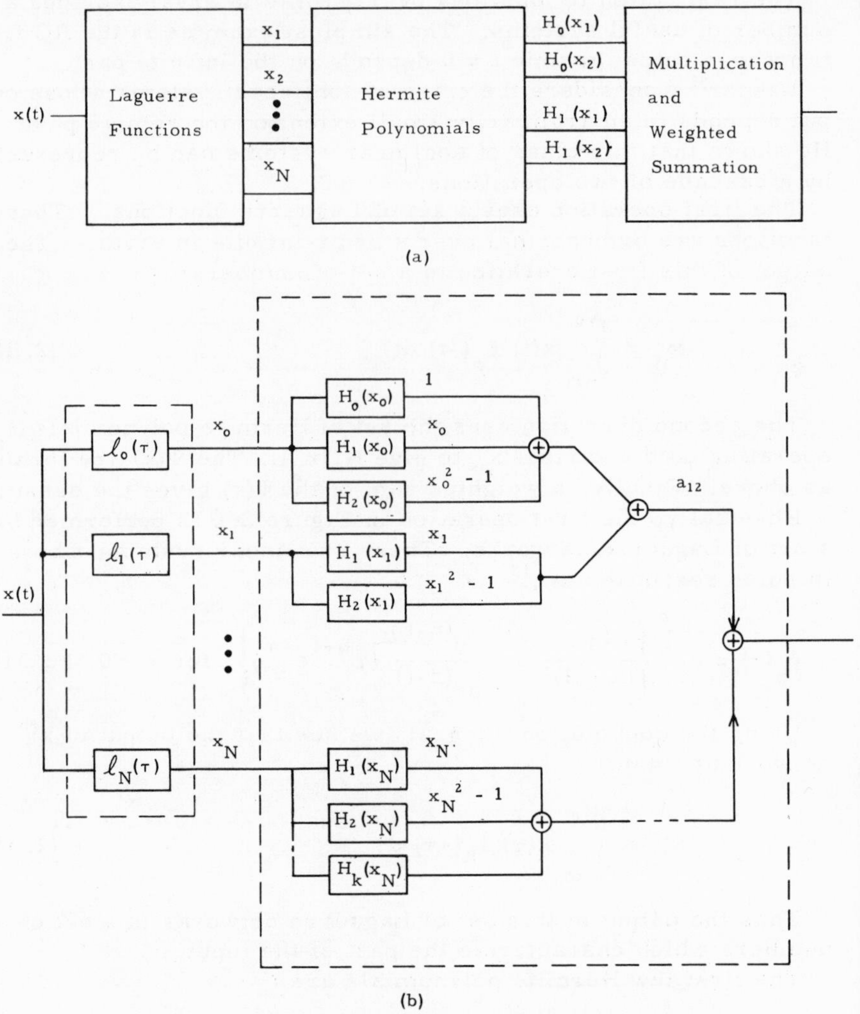

Figure 2. 6. Wiener network configuration

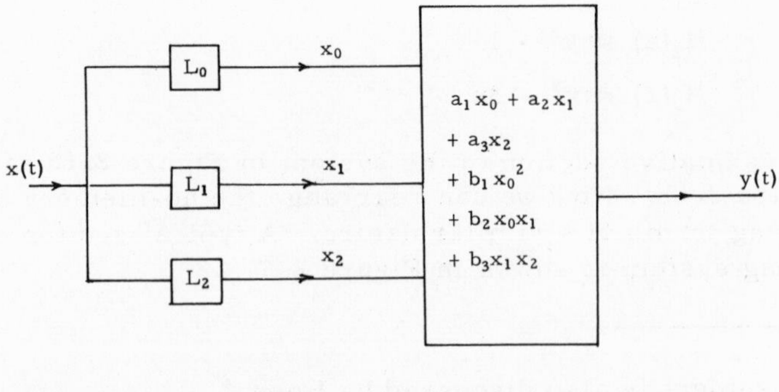

Figure 2. 7. A section from a Wiener network

Once the system is redrawn in this form, it is easy to show[8] the equivalence of the Wiener characterization and the Volterra functional expansion introduced in the first section of this chapter.

To summarize this equivalence briefly, consider the general Wiener network shown in Figure 2.6a and a simplified example of it in Figure 2.6b.

The nonlinear device shown in Figure 2.7 is easily described as a functional power series, since we have grouped together the terms of each order.

The linear part of y(t) can be written

$$y_1(t) = a_1 \int_{-\infty}^{\infty} L_0(\tau)\, x(t-\tau)\, d\tau + a_2 \int_{-\infty}^{\infty} L_1(\tau)\, x(t-\tau)\, d\tau + a_3 \int_{-\infty}^{\infty} L_2(\tau)\, x(t-\tau)\, d\tau \tag{2.33}$$

or by defining

$$K_1(\tau) = a_1 L_0(\tau) + a_2 L_1(\tau) + a_3 L_2(\tau) \tag{2.34}$$

we have

$$y_1(t) = \int_{-\infty}^{\infty} K_1(\tau)\, x(t-\tau)\, d\tau \tag{2.35}$$

Similarly, the quadratic part is

$$\begin{aligned} y_2(t) = {} & b_1 \int_{-\infty}^{\infty}\int_{-\infty}^{\infty} L_0(\tau_1)\, L_0(\tau_2)\, x(t-\tau_1)\, x(t-\tau_2)\, d\tau_1\, d\tau_2 \\ & + b_2 \int_{-\infty}^{\infty}\int_{-\infty}^{\infty} L_0(\tau_1)\, L_1(\tau_2)\, x(t-\tau_1)\, x(t-\tau_2)\, d\tau_1\, d\tau_2 \\ & + b_3 \int_{-\infty}^{\infty}\int_{-\infty}^{\infty} L_1(\tau_1)\, L_2(\tau_2)\, x(t-\tau_1)\, x(t-\tau_2)\, d\tau_1\, d\tau_2 \end{aligned} \tag{2.36}$$

or by defining

$$K_2(\tau_1, \tau_2) = b_1 L_0(\tau_1)\, L_0(\tau_2) + b_2 L_0(\tau_1)\, L_1(\tau_2) + b_3 L_1(\tau_1)\, L_2(\tau_2) \tag{2.37}$$

we have

$$y_2(t) = \int_{-\infty}^{\infty}\int_{-\infty}^{\infty} K_2(\tau_1, \tau_2)\, x(t-\tau_1)\, x(t-\tau_2)\, d\tau_1\, d\tau_2 \tag{2.38}$$

Thus, for the class of systems that Wiener considers, his characterization is equivalent to an expansion of the Volterra type.

Determining whether a system belongs to the Wiener class may sometimes be difficult. In all of the preceding examples the answer was obvious. Consider, however, the system whose phase-plane portrait is shown in Figure 2.8. This is an example of hard self-excitation.[28,1] The system has a stable equilibrium point and a stable limit cycle separated by an unstable limit cycle. Assume that this system is excited by an input which drives it outside the unstable limit cycle. Now if the input is removed, the system will move to the stable limit cycle and remain there. Alternately, assume that the system is excited by input which keeps it inside the unstable limit cycle. If the input is removed, the system moves to the stable equilibrium point. Here an input in the remote past has a definite effect on the system behavior. The system would not be included in Wiener's class. One can, however, show that there exists an analytic functional power series expansion around the stable equilibrium point.

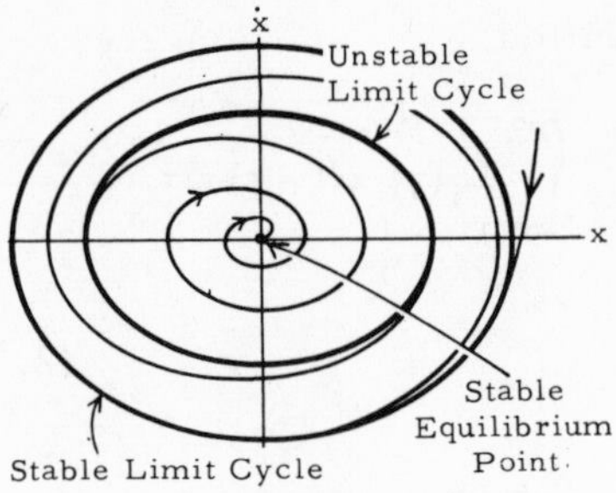

Figure 2.8. Phase-plane portrait (hard self-excitation)

In a general system there is no straightforward method to determine whether a limit cycle exists.

It appears that the solution to most optimization problems would lead to a nonlinear filter which could be realized without using feedback paths.† Thus, restricting ourselves to nonlinear systems which can be represented by a Volterra expansion is not serious.

3. Multidimensional Transform Theory

The advantages of Fourier and Laplace transforms in the analysis of linear systems are well known. One would expect similar advantages in the nonlinear case.

In the linear case, one defines the Fourier transform

---

† One exception is the maximum-likelihood estimator of signal phase.[32]

$$F(j\omega) = \int_{-\infty}^{\infty} f(t)\, e^{-j\omega t}\, dt \tag{2.39}$$

and its inverse

$$f(t) = \frac{1}{2\pi} \int_{-\infty}^{\infty} F(j\omega)\, e^{+j\omega t}\, d\omega \tag{2.40}$$

The transforms of the impulse responses in Figures 2.1 and 2.2 and the resulting s-plane plot (after analytic continuation) are shown in Figure 2.9. The shaded area indicates the region of convergence. To recover the time function, one may integrate along any vertical line in the region of convergence.

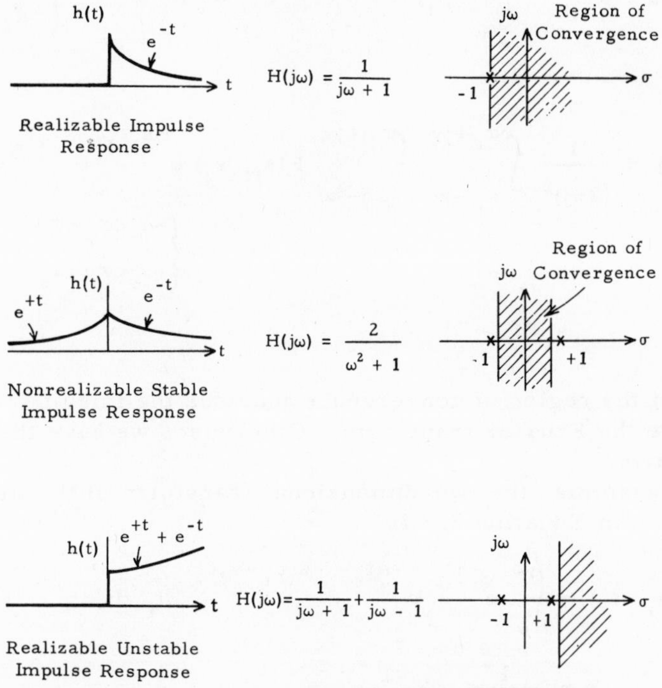

Figure 2.9. System functions

The realizable, unstable system in Figure 2.2b does not have a Fourier transform. Nevertheless, its Laplace transform exists as

$$\mathscr{L}(s) = \int_{-\infty}^{\infty} f(t)\, e^{-st}\, dt \qquad Re[s] > \sigma_0 \tag{2.41}$$

and

$$f(t) = \frac{1}{2\pi j} \int_{\sigma_1 - j\infty}^{\sigma_1 + j\infty} \mathscr{L}(s)\, e^{+st}\, ds \qquad \sigma_1 > \sigma_0 \tag{2.42}$$

The Laplace transform and the corresponding pole plot of the system in Figure 2.2b are shown in Figure 2.9. Note that the two pole plots are the same but the regions of convergence are different. The importance of the region of convergence when dealing with unrealizable and unstable linear systems is well known.[25]

For multidimensional kernels, one uses the corresponding multidimensional transform relation.

For two dimensions, we have

$$F(s_1, s_2) = \int_{-\infty}^{\infty} \int_{-\infty}^{\infty} f(t_1, t_2)\, e^{-s_1 t_1}\, e^{-s_2 t_2}\, dt_1\, dt_2 \qquad \begin{cases} -\sigma_0 < \mathrm{Re}[s_1] < \sigma_1 \\ -\sigma_2 < \mathrm{Re}[s_2] < \sigma_3 \end{cases} \tag{2.43}$$

and

$$f(t_1, t_2) = \frac{1}{(2\pi j)^2} \int_{\sigma_\alpha - j\infty}^{\sigma_\alpha + j\infty} \int_{\sigma_\beta - j\infty}^{\sigma_\beta + j\infty} F(s_1, s_2)\, e^{+s_1 t_1}\, e^{+s_2 t_2}\, ds_1\, ds_2 \qquad \begin{cases} -\sigma_0 < \sigma_\alpha < \sigma_1 \\ -\sigma_2 < \sigma_\beta < \sigma_3 \end{cases} \tag{2.44}$$

When the region of convergence includes the imaginary axis, we have the Fourier transform. Otherwise, we have the Laplace transform.

For example, the two-dimensional transform of the impulse response in Equation 2.7 is

$$H(s_1, s_2) = \int_0^{\infty} e^{-\alpha t_1}\, e^{-\alpha t_2}\, e^{-s_1 t_1 - s_2 t_2}\, dt_1\, dt_2$$

$$= \frac{1}{s_1 + \alpha} \cdot \frac{1}{s_2 + \alpha} \tag{2.45}$$

Clearly, the transforms of separable impulse responses are separable.

Most of the properties of the one-dimensional transform carry over to the multidimensional case. The derivation of most of these properties was done by George.[11] We shall develop several properties that we shall need specifically.

First, consider the frequency domain counterpart to the

convolution indicated in Equation 2.6:

$$z(t) = \int_{-\infty}^{\infty}\int_{-\infty}^{\infty} h_2(\tau_1, \tau_2)\, x(t - \tau_1)\, x(t - \tau_2)\, d\tau_1\, d\tau_2 \tag{2.46}$$

The corresponding transforms are

$$H_2(s_1, s_2) = \int_{-\infty}^{\infty}\int_{-\infty}^{\infty} h_2(\tau_1, \tau_2)\, e^{-s_1t_1 - s_2t_2}\, dt_1\, dt_2 \tag{2.47}$$

$$X(s) = \int_{-\infty}^{\infty} x(t)\, e^{-st}\, dt \tag{2.48}$$

Now one introduces the variables t_1 and t_2 into Equation 2.46:

$$z(t_1, t_2) = \int_{-\infty}^{\infty}\int_{-\infty}^{\infty} h_2(\tau_1, \tau_2)\, x(t_1 - \tau_1)\, x(t_1 - \tau_2)\, d\tau_1\, d\tau_2 \tag{2.49}$$

where $z(t)$, the desired time function, equals $z(t_1, t_2)$ when $t_1 = t_2$.

Substituting into Equation 2.49 and transforming, we have

$$Z(s_1, s_2) = H_2(s_1, s_2)\, X(s_1)\, X(s_2) \tag{2.50}$$

To get $z(t)$, we obtain the inverse transform $z(t_1, t_2)$ and set $t_1 = t_2$.

Second,[5] consider the cascade of a second-order system and a linear system. In the time domain,

$$z(t) = \int_{-\infty}^{\infty} C_1(t - \tau)\, y(\tau)\, d\tau$$

$$= \int_{-\infty}^{\infty} C_1(t - \tau)\, d\tau \int_{-\infty}^{\infty}\int_{-\infty}^{\infty} H_2(\tau - \tau_1, \tau - \tau_2)\, x(\tau_1)\, x(\tau_2)\, d\tau_1\, d\tau_2 \tag{2.51}$$

The corresponding relation in the transform domain is

$$Z(s_1, s_2) = C_1(s_1 + s_2)\, H_2(s_1, s_2)\, X(s_1)\, X(s_2) \tag{2.52}$$

Third, consider the operation of repeated differentiation:

$$z(t) = \frac{d}{dt}\int_{-\infty}^{\infty} h_1(t - \tau)\, x(\tau)\, d\tau \tag{2.53}$$

In the transform domain, we have

$$Z(s) = s\, H_1(s)\, X(s) \tag{2.54}$$

For a second-order kernel,

$$z(t) = \frac{d}{dt}\int_{-\infty}^{\infty}\int_{-\infty}^{\infty} h_2(t - \tau_1, t - \tau_2)\, x(\tau_1)\, x(\tau_2)\, d\tau_1\, d\tau_2 \qquad (2.55)$$

This operation corresponds to

$$z(s_1, s_2) = (s_1 + s_2)\, H_2(s_1, s_2)\, X(s_1)\, X(s_2) \qquad (2.56)$$

The corresponding relations for a more general linear operation on a function follow directly. For example, if

$$L = a\frac{d^2}{dt^2} + b\frac{d}{dt} + c \qquad (2.57)$$

then

$(as^2 + bs + c)\, H_1(s)\, X(s)$

corresponds to

$$\left(a\frac{d^2}{dt^2} + b\frac{d}{dt} + c\right)\int_{-\infty}^{\infty} h_1(t - \tau)\, x(\tau)\, d\tau \qquad (2.58)$$

and

$[a(s_1 + s_2 + s_3)^2 + b(s_1 + s_2 + s_3) + c]\, H_3(s_1, s_2, s_3)\, X(s_1)\, X(s_2)\, X(s_3)$

corresponds to

$$\left(a\frac{d^2}{dt^2} + b\frac{d}{dt} + c\right)$$

$$\int_{-\infty}^{\infty}\int_{-\infty}^{\infty}\int_{-\infty}^{\infty} h_3(t - \tau_1, t - \tau_2, t - \tau_3)\, x(\tau_1)\, x(\tau_2)\, x(\tau_3)\, d\tau_1\, d\tau_2\, d\tau_3$$

$$(2.59)$$

Thus one can write the transform as the product of the transform of the operator (with the correct dimensionality) and the transform of the function.

All of these properties hold for an n-dimensional transform.

We shall see in Chapter 3 that our approach will be primarily in the transform domain. The starting point will be a set of transforms corresponding to some set of realizable, stable multidimensional kernels. We should like to be able to check these kernel transforms for realizability and stability in the frequency domain. In the next section, we shall describe some important properties of the transforms.

4. Properties of the Transforms of Multidimensional Kernels†

We shall develop the following properties of higher-dimensional kernels which correspond to impulse responses:

(1) The form of transform that is necessary for the corresponding impulse response to be a real function.
(2) The nonlinear analog to real part sufficiency and a generalized Hilbert transform relation.
(3) The constraint between the gain and minimum-phase relations in each kernel.
(4) A criterion to test the realizability of an nth-order gain function.
(5) Necessary and sufficient conditions for the stability of a straightforward method of testing stability of rational transforms.

As would be expected, the approach to the problem is a generalization of the approach to the properties of linear transforms described by Lee[15] and Mason.[21] The transform pair that we shall use is

$$K(s_1, s_2) = \int_{-\infty}^{\infty}\int_{-\infty}^{\infty} k(t_1, t_2)\, e^{-s_1t_1}\, e^{-s_2t_2}\, dt_1\, dt_2 \qquad (2.60)$$

$$k(t_1, t_2) = \left(\frac{1}{2\pi j}\right)^2 \int_{-j\infty}^{+j\infty}\int_{-j\infty}^{+j\infty} K(s_1, s_2)\, e^{+s_1t_1}\, e^{+s_2t_2}\, ds_1\, ds_2 \qquad (2.61)$$

where $s_1 = \sigma_1 + j\omega_1$, $s_2 = \sigma_2 + j\omega_2$. We are concerned in general with functions whose region of convergence includes the imaginary axis in each variable, so that the Fourier transform is included in our definition. All properties will be illustrated by the two-dimensional case and the necessary generalization for the nth-order case indicated.

The first property follows trivially from Equation 2.60. If we consider s_1, s_2 to be real variables, then the integrand is a real function for all real impulse responses. This implies that $K(s_1, s_2)$ has the form of a real function of s_1 and s_2. Thus the most general rational transform for a real second-order impulse response is

---

† The first three sections were a review of some concepts needed to understand our approach. The work beginning here is original.

$$K(s_1, s_2) = \frac{\sum_{i=0}^{N} \sum_{j=0}^{N} a_{ij} s_1^i s_2^j}{\sum_{i=0}^{M} \sum_{j=0}^{M} b_{ij} s_1^i s_2^j} \tag{2.62}$$

where a_{ij} and b_{ij} are real coefficients. Since any kernel can be made symmetrical, $a_{ij} = a_{ji}$ and $b_{ij} = b_{ji}$.

Let us now consider realizable impulse responses and their properties.

Realizable Impulse Responses. Let $k(t_1, t_2) = 0$ for either t_1 or $t_2 < 0$. A typical response is shown in Figure 2.10. We

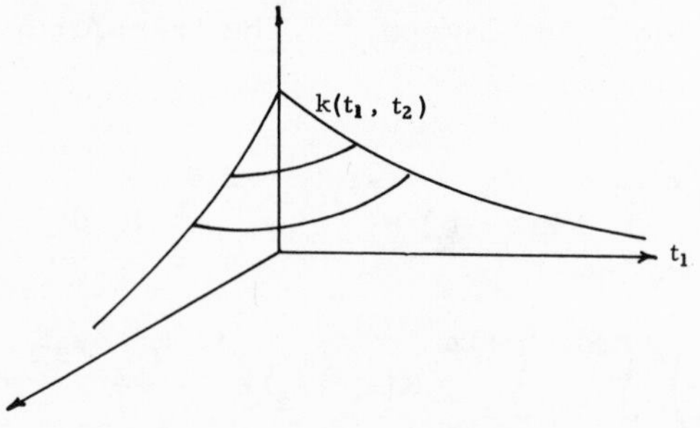

Figure 2.10. Realizable impulse response

can write

$$k_2(t_1, t_2) = k_2^{I}(t_1^E, t_2^E) + k_2^{II}(t_1^E, t_2^O) + k_2^{III}(t_1^O, t_2^O) + k_2^{IV}(t_1^O, t_2^E) \tag{2.63}$$

where $k_2^{I}(t_1^E, t_2^E)$ denotes a function that is even with respect to the variables t_1 and t_2, as shown in Figure 2.11. We exclude the singularity function $u_0(t_1)\, u_0(t_2)$ and its derivatives from our class of $k_2(t_1, t_2)$ that is to be considered. For a realizable system it follows that

$$k_2^{I}(t_1^E, t_2^E) = k_2^{II}(t_1^E, t_2^O) = k_2^{III}(t_1^O, t_2^O) = k_2^{IV}(t_1^O, t_2^E) = \frac{1}{4} k_2(t_1, t_2) \qquad \text{for } t_1, t_2 \geq 0 \tag{2.64}$$

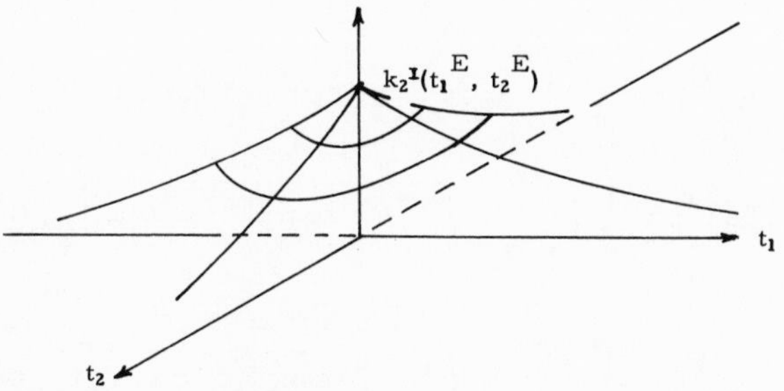

Figure 2.11. Even part of impulse response

Substituting Equation 2.63 in the direct Fourier transform equation gives

$$K_2(j\omega_1, j\omega_2) = \int_{-\infty}^{\infty}\int_{-\infty}^{\infty}\left[k_2^{I}(t_1^E, t_2^E) + k_2^{II}(t_1^O, t_2^O) + k_2^{III}(t_1^O, t_2^E) + k_2^{IV}(t_1^E, t_2^O)\right] \times \left[\cos\omega_1 t_1 \cos\omega_2 t_2 - \sin\omega_1 t_1 \sin\omega_2 t_2 - j\sin\omega_1 t_1 \cos\omega_2 t_2 - j\sin\omega_2 t_2 \cos\omega_1 t_1\right] dt_1\, dt_2 \tag{2.65}$$

Taking advantage of the oddness and evenness of the various terms in the integrand, we have

$$\begin{aligned} K_2(j\omega_1, j\omega_2) = &\int_{-\infty}^{\infty}\int_{-\infty}^{\infty} k_2^{I}(t_1^E, t_2^E) \cos\omega_1 t_1 \cos\omega_2 t_2\, dt_1\, dt_2 \\ &- \int_{-\infty}^{\infty}\int_{-\infty}^{\infty} k_2^{II}(t_1^O, t_2^O) \sin\omega_1 t_1 \sin\omega_2 t_2\, dt_1\, dt_2 \\ &- j\int_{-\infty}^{\infty}\int_{-\infty}^{\infty} k_2^{III}(t_1^O, t_2^E) \sin\omega_1 t_1 \cos\omega_2 t_2\, dt_1\, dt_2 \\ &- j\int_{-\infty}^{\infty}\int_{-\infty}^{\infty} k_2^{IV}(t_1^O, t_2^E) \sin\omega_1 t_1 \cos\omega_2 t_2\, dt_1\, dt_2 \end{aligned} \tag{2.66}$$

By dividing $K_2(j\omega_1, j\omega_2)$ into its real and imaginary parts and then into even and odd parts, we have

$$K_2(j\omega_1, j\omega_2) = K_R(j\omega_1^E, j\omega_2^E) + K_R(j\omega_1^O, j\omega_2^O) + j\,K_I(j\omega_1^O, j\omega_2^E) + j\,K_I(j\omega_1^E, j\omega_2^E) \tag{2.67}$$

where

$$K_R(j\omega_1^E, j\omega_2^E) = \int_0^\infty \int_0^\infty k_2(t_1, t_2) \cos \omega_1 t_1 \cos \omega_2 t_2 \, dt_1 \, dt_2 \quad (2.68)$$

$$K_R(j\omega_1^O, j\omega_2^O) = -\int_0^\infty \int_0^\infty k_2(t_1, t_2) \sin \omega_1 t_1 \sin \omega_2 t_2 \, dt_1 \, dt_2 \quad (2.69)$$

$$K_I(j\omega_1^O, j\omega_2^E) = -\int_0^\infty \int_0^\infty k_2(t_1, t_2) \sin \omega_1 t_1 \cos \omega_2 t_2 \, dt_1 \, dt_2 \quad (2.70)$$

in which symmetry has been used to change the limits of integration.

Clearly, then, the inverse transform for either Equation 2.68, 2.69, or 2.70 can be used to find $k_2(t_1, t_2)$. For example,

$$k_2(t_1, t_2) = \left(\frac{1}{2\pi}\right)^2 \int_0^\infty \int_0^\infty K_R(j\omega_1^E, j\omega_2^E) \cos \omega_1 t_1 \cos \omega_2 t_2 \, d\omega_1 \, d\omega_2 \quad (2.71)$$

The conclusion is that any one of the four parts of a second-order transform is sufficient to specify the corresponding realizable impulse response. Similarly, for n = 3, the transform divides into eight parts:

$$\begin{aligned} K_3(j\omega_1, j\omega_2, j\omega_3) = {} & K_R(\omega_1^E, \omega_2^E, \omega_3^E) + K_R(\omega_1^E, \omega_2^O, \omega_3^O) \\ & + K_R(\omega_1^O, \omega_2^E, \omega_3^O) + K_R(\omega_1^O, \omega_2^O, \omega_3^E) \\ & + j \Big[K_I(\omega_1^O, \omega_2^O, \omega_3^O) + K_I(\omega_1^O, \omega_2^E, \omega_3^E) \\ & + K_I(\omega_1^E, \omega_2^O, \omega_3^E) + K_I(\omega_1^E, \omega_2^E, \omega_3^O) \Big] \end{aligned} \quad (2.72)$$

and any one of the eight parts is sufficient to specify the corresponding realizable impulse response.

Since $K_R(j\omega_1^E, j\omega_2^E)$ completely determines the transform, we should expect that there exists a generalized Hilbert transform relation that expresses $K_R(j\omega_1^O, j\omega_2^O)$, $K_I(j\omega_1^O, j\omega_2^E)$, and $K_1(j\omega_1^E, j\omega_2^O)$ as explicit functions of $K_R(j\omega_1^E, j\omega_2^E)$, and vice versa. The derivation of a typical relation of this kind will be given in the next section.

Generalized Hilbert Transform. Let $k(t_1, t_2)$ be an arbitrary, realizable kernel that is Fourier-transformable. Let

$$k(t_1, t_2) = (2\pi)^2 f(t_1, t_2) \, d(t_1, t_2) \qquad \text{for all } t_1, t_2 \quad (2.73)$$

We can choose $f(t_1, t_2)$ to be any realizable function as long as it is not zero at any point where $k(t_1, t_2)$ is nonzero. This will specify $d(t_1, t_2)$ in the $t_1, t_2 > 0$.

The relation corresponding to Equation 2.73 in the transform domain is

$$K(j\omega_3, j\omega_4) = \int_{-\infty}^{\infty}\int_{-\infty}^{\infty} F(j\omega_3 - j\omega_1, j\omega_4 - j\omega_2)\, D(j\omega_1, j\omega_2)\, d\omega_1\, d\omega_2 \tag{2.74}$$

Let

$$f(t_1, t_2) = \left(\frac{1}{\pi}\right)^2 u_{-1}(t_1)\, e^{-a_1 t_1}\, u_{-1}(t_2)\, e^{-a_2 t_2} \tag{2.75}$$

Then

$$F(j\omega_1, j\omega_2) = \left(\frac{1}{\pi}\right)^2 \frac{a_1 - j\omega_1}{a_1^2 + \omega_1^2} \cdot \frac{a_2 - j\omega_2}{a_2^2 + \omega_2^2} = \left(\frac{1}{\pi}\right)^2 \frac{a_1 a_2 - \omega_1\omega_2 - j(a_1\omega_2 + a_2\omega_1)}{(a_1^2 + \omega_1^2)(a_2^2 + \omega_2^2)} \tag{2.76}$$

Note that since $k(t_1, t_2)$ is symmetrical in its arguments, if $a_1 = a_2$, then $d(t_1, t_2)$ will be symmetrical. Since $d(t_1, t_2)$ is arbitrary for either $t_1, t_2 < 0$, we can make it an even function in both arguments. This implies that $D(j\omega_1, j\omega_2)$ is real and even in both arguments; thus

$$K(j\omega_3, j\omega_4) = \int_{-\infty}^{\infty}\int_{-\infty}^{\infty} \left(\frac{1}{\pi}\right)^2 \frac{a_1 - j(\omega_3 - \omega_1)}{a_1^2 + (\omega_3 - \omega_1)^2} \cdot \frac{a_2 - j(\omega_4 - \omega_2)}{a_2^2 + (\omega_4 - \omega_2)^2} \cdot D(j\omega_1, j\omega_2)\, d\omega_1\, d\omega_2 \tag{2.77}$$

Since $D(j\omega_1, j\omega_2)$ is real, we have

$$K_R(j\omega_3, j\omega_4) = \left(\frac{1}{\pi}\right)^2 \int_{-\infty}^{\infty}\int_{-\infty}^{\infty} \frac{a_1 a_2 - (\omega_3 - \omega_1)(\omega_4 - \omega_2)}{\left[a_1^2 + (\omega_3 - \omega_1)^2\right]\left[a_2^2 + (\omega_4 - \omega_2)^2\right]} \cdot D(j\omega_1, j\omega_2)\, d\omega_1\, d\omega_2 \tag{2.78}$$

Since $D(j\omega_1, j\omega_2)$ is even in both arguments, the even part of $F_R(j\omega_1, j\omega_2)$ gives the even part of $K_R(j\omega_3, j\omega_4)$, so that

$$K_R(j\omega_3^E, j\omega_4^E) = \left(\frac{1}{\pi}\right)^2 \int_{-\infty}^{\infty}\int_{-\infty}^{\infty} \frac{a_1 a_2}{\left[a_1^2 + (\omega_3 - \omega_1)^2\right]\left[a_2^2 + (\omega_4 - \omega_2)^2\right]} \cdot D(j\omega_1, j\omega_2)\, d\omega_1\, d\omega_2 \tag{2.79}$$

Similarly,

$$K_I(j\omega_3{}^O, j\omega_4{}^E) = \left(\frac{1}{\pi}\right)^2 \int_{-\infty}^{\infty}\int_{-\infty}^{\infty} \frac{-a_2(\omega_3-\omega_1)}{\left[a_1{}^2+(\omega_3-\omega_1)^2\right]\left[a_2{}^2+(\omega_4-\omega_2)^2\right]}$$

$$\cdot D(j\omega_1, j\omega_2)\, d\omega_1\, d\omega_2 \tag{2.80}$$

Let $a_1 = a_2 \to 0$. Then

$$\frac{a_1}{a_1{}^2+(\omega_3-\omega_1)^2} \to \pi u_0(\omega_3-\omega_1) \tag{2.81}$$

$$\frac{a_2}{a_2{}^2+(\omega_4-\omega_2)^2} \to \pi u_0(\omega_4-\omega_2) \tag{2.82}$$

and Equation 2.79 becomes

$$K_R(j\omega_3{}^E, j\omega_4{}^E) = D(j\omega_3, j\omega_4) \tag{2.83}$$

In Equation 2.80,

$$\frac{\omega_3-\omega_1}{a_1{}^2+(\omega_3-\omega_1)^2} \to \frac{1}{\omega_3-\omega_1} \tag{2.84}$$

and hence we obtain

$$K_I(j\omega_3{}^O, j\omega_4{}^E) = -\frac{1}{\pi}\int_{-\infty}^{\infty} \frac{1}{\omega_3-\omega_1} \cdot D(j\omega_1, j\omega_4)\, d\omega \tag{2.85}$$

or

$$K_I(j\omega_3{}^O, j\omega_4{}^E) = -\frac{1}{\pi}\int_{-\infty}^{\infty} \frac{1}{\omega_3-\omega_1} \cdot K_R(j\omega_1{}^E, j\omega_4{}^E)\, d\omega_1 \tag{2.86}$$

The complete imaginary part is

$$K_I(j\omega_3, j\omega_4) = K_I(j\omega_3{}^O, j\omega_4{}^E) + K_I(j\omega_3{}^E, j\omega_4{}^O) \tag{2.87}$$

where the second term follows directly from symmetry.

In retrospect, we note that Equation 2.86 could have been obtained by equating the inverse transforms of Equations 2.68 and 2.70:

$$\int_0^\infty \int_0^\infty K_R(j\omega_1{}^E, j\omega_2{}^E) \cos \omega_1 t_1 \cos \omega_2 t_2 \, d\omega_1 \, d\omega_2$$

$$= -\int_0^\infty \int_0^\infty K_I(j\omega_1{}^O, j\omega_2{}^E) \sin \omega_1 t_1 \cos \omega_2 t_2 \, dt_1 \, dt_2 \quad (2.88)$$

or

$$\int_0^\infty \cos \omega_2 t_2 \, d\omega_2 \int_0^\infty K_R(j\omega_1{}^E, j\omega_2{}^E) \cos \omega_1 t_1 \, d\omega_1$$

$$= -\int_0^\infty \cos \omega_2 t_2 \, d\omega_2 \int_0^\infty K_I(j\omega_1{}^O, j\omega_2{}^E) \sin \omega_1 t_1 \, d\omega_1 \quad (2.89)$$

but because the outer transform relation is unique we have

$$\int_0^\infty K_R(j\omega_1{}^E, j\omega_2{}^E) \cos \omega_1 t_1 \, d\omega_1 = -\int_0^\infty K_I(j\omega_1{}^O, j\omega_2{}^E) \sin \omega_1 t_1 \, d\omega_1 \quad (2.90)$$

This is analogous to the linear relation with an arbitrary ω_2. Thus we can write Equation 2.87 directly.

The corresponding relation follows in similar fashion:

$$K_R(j\omega_3{}^E, j\omega_4{}^E) = +\frac{1}{\pi} \int_{-\infty}^{\infty} \frac{1}{\omega_3 - \omega_1} \cdot K_I(j\omega_1{}^O, j\omega_4{}^E) \, d\omega_1 \quad (2.91)$$

Similar reasoning leads to a useful constraint relation between the odd and even parts of the real part of $K(j\omega_1, j\omega_2)$:

$$K_R(j\omega_1{}^O, j\omega_2{}^O) = \frac{1}{\pi^2} \int_{-\infty}^{\infty} \int_{-\infty}^{\infty} \frac{1}{\omega_1 - \omega_3} \cdot \frac{1}{\omega_2 - \omega_4} K_R(j\omega_3{}^E, j\omega_4{}^E) \, d\omega_3 \, d\omega_4 \quad (2.92)$$

Our Hilbert transform relation can be put into a more useful form, if we consider Equation 2.86 and a second analogous relation:

$$K_I(j\omega_3{}^O, j\omega_4{}^E) = -\frac{1}{\pi} \int_{-\infty}^{\infty} \frac{1}{\omega_3 - \omega_1} \cdot K_R(j\omega_1{}^E, j\omega_4{}^E) \, d\omega_1 \quad (2.86)$$

$$K_I(j\omega_3{}^E, j\omega_4{}^O) = -\frac{1}{\pi} \int_{-\infty}^{\infty} \frac{1}{\omega_3 - \omega_1} \cdot K_R(j\omega_1{}^O, j\omega_4{}^O) \, d\omega_1 \quad (2.93)$$

Adding the two equations, we get

$$K_I(j\omega_3, j\omega_4) = -\frac{1}{\pi}\int_{-\infty}^{\infty} \frac{K_R(j\omega_1, j\omega_4)}{\omega_3 - \omega_1} d\omega_1 \tag{2.94}$$

In order for Equation 2.94 to be correct, it is necessary that both $K_R(j\omega_1^E, j\omega_2^E)$ and $K_R(j\omega_1^O, j\omega_2^O)$ not be identically zero. A simple example illustrates the difficulty when $K_R(j\omega_1^O, j\omega_2^O)$ is identically zero. Let

$$K_2(j\omega_1, j\omega_2) = \frac{1}{1 + j\omega_1} + \frac{1}{1 + j\omega_2} = \frac{1 - j\omega_1}{1 + \omega_1^2} + \frac{1 - j\omega_2}{1 + \omega_2^2} \tag{2.95}$$

$$K_2(j\omega_1^E, j\omega_2^E) = \frac{1}{1 + \omega_1^2} + \frac{1}{1 + \omega_2^2} \tag{2.96}$$

Using Equation 2.86, we obtain

$$K_I(\omega_3^O, \omega_2^E) = -\frac{1}{\pi}\int_{-\infty}^{\infty} \frac{1}{\omega_3 - \omega_1}\left\{\frac{1}{1 + \omega_1^2} + \frac{1}{1 + \omega_2^2}\right\} d\omega_1 \tag{2.97}$$

Expanding in partial fractions, we have

$$K_I(\omega_3^O, \omega_2^E) = -\frac{1}{\pi}\int_{-\infty}^{\infty}\left[\frac{\frac{1}{1 + \omega_3^2}}{\omega_3 - \omega_1} + \frac{\frac{\omega_1}{1 + \omega_3^2}}{1 + \omega_1^2} + \frac{\frac{\omega_3}{1 + \omega_3^2}}{1 + \omega_1^2} + \frac{\frac{1}{1 + \omega_2^2}}{\omega_3 - \omega_1}\right] d\omega_1 \tag{2.98}$$

The first, second, and fourth terms are zero because of symmetry. Integrating the third term gives

$$K_I(j\omega_3^O, j\omega_2^E) = \frac{-\omega_3}{1 + \omega_3^2} \tag{2.99}$$

From symmetry we know that

$$K_I(j\omega_3^E, j\omega_2^O) = \frac{-\omega_2}{1 + \omega_2^2} \tag{2.100}$$

If we had applied Equation 2.94 directly, the term in Equation 2.100 would have been omitted. For symmetrical kernels, the omission is obvious.

In a similar fashion, we can show that if all of the terms in Equation 2.72 are nonzero, then the relationship for third-order kernels is

$$K_I(j\omega_1, j\omega_2, j\omega_3) = -\frac{1}{\pi}\int_{-\infty}^{\infty} \frac{K_R(\omega_4, \omega_2, \omega_3)}{\omega_1 - \omega_4}\, d\omega_4 \qquad (2.101)$$

Although the derivation was straightforward, the result is at first rather surprising. We have shown that, except for a few special cases, we can determine the imaginary part of an nth-order transform from the real part by a single integration.

By looking at the transform in a different way, we can see why this is true. An arbitrary third-order kernel can be constructed by using a complete set of orthogonal linear networks and performing no-memory operations on their output. Consider the system shown in Figure 2.12. A typical no-memory operation

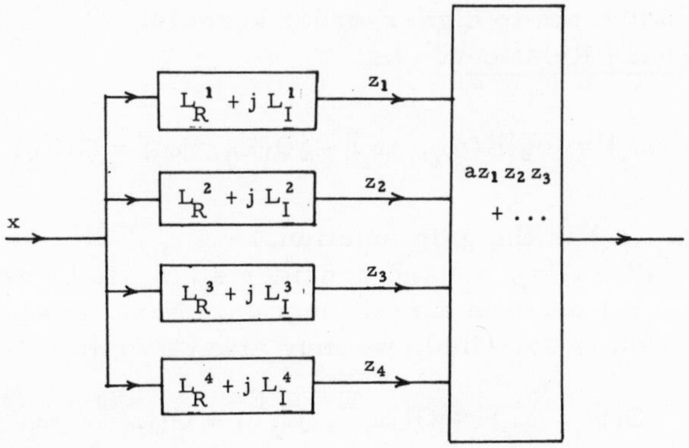

Figure 2.12. Third-order kernel

is $az_1z_2z_3$. The part of the kernel represented by this operation is

$$\begin{aligned} K_3^{a}(j\omega_1, j\omega_2, j\omega_3) = {} & L_R^1(j\omega_1)\, L_R^2(j\omega_2)\, L_R^3(j\omega_3) + jL_I^1(j\omega_1)\, L_R^2(j\omega_2)\, L_R^3(j\omega_3) \\ & - L_I^1(j\omega_1)\, L_I^2(j\omega_2)\, L_R^3(j\omega_3) + jL_R^1(j\omega_1)\, L_I^2(j\omega_2)\, L_R^3(j\omega_3) \\ & - L_R^1(j\omega_1)\, L_I^2(j\omega_2)\, L_I^3(j\omega_3) - jL_I^1(j\omega_1)\, L_I^2(j\omega_2)\, L_I^3(j\omega_3) \\ & - L_I^1(j\omega_1)\, L_R^2(j\omega_2)\, L_I^3(j\omega_3) + jL_R^1(j\omega_1)\, L_R^2(j\omega_2)\, L_I^3(j\omega_3) \end{aligned}$$

(2.102)

Looking at each pair of terms, we see that just by using familiar linear relations, each imaginary term can be obtained from the real term preceding it by the same Hilbert transform pair:

$$\text{Imaginary term} = -\frac{1}{\pi}\int_{-\infty}^{\infty} \frac{\text{Real term}}{\omega_1 - \omega_4}\, d\omega_4 \qquad (2.103)$$

The most general third-order kernel can be approximated arbitrarily closely by using a sufficiently large number of operations identical in form to the one just described. By recalling the equality in Equation 2.104,

$$\sum_{a=1}^{N} \text{Re}\left[K_3^{\,a}(j\omega_1,\ j\omega_2,\ j\omega_3)\right] = \text{Re}\left[\sum_{a=1}^{N} K_3^{\,a}(j\omega_1,\ j\omega_2,\ j\omega_3)\right] \qquad (2.104)$$

our previous result follows logically.

The next step is to generalize the idea of gain-phase relations in linear networks to higher-order kernels.

Gain-Phase Relations. Let

$$\log K(j\omega_1,\ j\omega_2) = \log|K(j\omega_1,\ j\omega_2)| + j\Theta(j\omega_1,\ j\omega_2) = G(j\omega_1,\ j\omega_2) + j\Theta(j\omega_1,\ j\omega_2) \qquad (2.105)$$

where $G(\omega_1,\ \omega_2)$ is the gain function.

First, write $G(s_1,\ s_2)$ and consider s_1, s_2 to be real variables. Then $G(s_1,\ s_2)$ must be a real function. Next, assuming that this condition is satisfied, we may always write

$$G(j\omega_1,\ j\omega_2) = G(j\omega_1^{\,E},\ j\omega_2^{\,E}) + G(j\omega_1^{\,O},\ j\omega_2^{\,O}) \qquad (2.106)$$

Applying the Hilbert transform of Equation 2.86 will give a phase function $\Theta(j\omega_1^{\,O},\ j\omega_2^{\,E})$. Symmetry gives $\Theta(j\omega_1^{\,E},\ j\omega_2^{\,O})$. The resultant function $\log K(j\omega_1,\ j\omega_2)$ has all of the necessary properties of a realizable, stable system function.

Clearly, if $\log K(j\omega_1,\ j\omega_2)$ is a realizable, stable system function, then $K(j\omega_1,\ j\omega_2)$ and $\dfrac{1}{K(j\omega_1,\ j\omega_2)}$ are also realizable and stable.

As in the preceding section, if both $G(j\omega_1^{\,E},\ j\omega_2^{\,E})$ and $G(j\omega_1^{\,O},\ j\omega_2^{\,O})$ are nonzero, then the relation

$$\Theta(j\omega_3,\ j\omega_4) = -\frac{1}{\pi}\int_{-\infty}^{\infty} \frac{1}{\omega_3 - \omega_1}\, G(j\omega_1,\ j\omega_2)\, d\omega_1 \qquad (2.107)$$

holds.

In connection with this restriction, we can show a property that is also useful for other purposes. The symmetrical kernels $G(j\omega_1^{\,O},\ j\omega_2^{\,O}) \equiv 0$ if and only if the kernel is separable.

First, we shall show that a separable kernel implies that $G(j\omega_1{}^O, j\omega_2{}^O) \equiv 0$.

Let the separable kernel be

$$H(j\omega_1, j\omega_2) = H_A(j\omega_1)\, H_B(j\omega_2) \tag{2.108}$$

The gain is

$$\begin{aligned} G(j\omega_1, j\omega_2) &= \log |H_A(j\omega_1)\, H_B(j\omega_2)| \\ &= \frac{1}{2} \log [H_A(j\omega_1)\, H_A(-j\omega_1)\, H_B(j\omega_2)\, H_B(-j\omega_2)] \end{aligned} \tag{2.109}$$

The odd part of $G(j\omega_1, j\omega_2)$ is

$$G(j\omega_1{}^O, j\omega_2{}^O = \frac{1}{2} [G(j\omega_1, j\omega_2) - G(-j\omega_1, j\omega_2)] \tag{2.110}$$

or

$$\begin{aligned} 4\,G(j\omega_1{}^O, j\omega_2{}^O) &= \log [H_A(j\omega_1)\, H_A(-j\omega_1)\, H_B(j\omega_2)\, H_B(-j\omega_2)] \\ &\quad - \log [H_A(-j\omega_1)\, H_A(+j\omega_1)\, H_B(+j\omega_2)\, H_B(-j\omega_2)] \end{aligned} \tag{2.111}$$

$$4\,G(j\omega_1{}^O, j\omega_2{}^O) = \log \left\{ \frac{H_A(j\omega_1)\, H_A(-j\omega_1)\, H_B(j\omega_2)\, H_B(-j\omega_2)}{H_A(-j\omega_1)\, H_A(+j\omega_1)\, H_B(+j\omega_2)\, H_B(-j\omega_2)} \right\} \equiv 0 \tag{2.112}$$

To prove the converse, consider a nonseparable kernel, $H(j\omega_1, j\omega_2)$. Using the same approach, we have

$$4\,G(j\omega_1{}^O, j\omega_2{}^O) = \log \left\{ \frac{H(j\omega_1, j\omega_2)\, H(-j\omega_1, -j\omega_2)}{H(-j\omega_1, +j\omega_2)\, H(-j\omega_1, +j\omega_2)} \right\} \tag{2.113}$$

Assume that $G(j\omega_1{}^O, j\omega_2{}^O) = 0$. If H is not separable, then this implies that

$$H(j\omega_1, j\omega_2) = H(-j\omega_1, j\omega_2) \tag{2.114}$$

or

$$H_R(j\omega_1, j\omega_2) + jH_I(j\omega_1, j\omega_2) = H_R(-j\omega_1, j\omega_2) + jH_I(-j\omega_1, j\omega_2) \tag{2.115}$$

or

$$H_R(j\omega_1, j\omega_2) - H_R(-j\omega_1, j\omega_2) = 2\,H_R(j\omega_1{}^O, j\omega_2{}^O) = 0 \tag{2.116}$$

and

$$H_I(j\omega_1, j\omega_2) - H_I(-j\omega_1, j\omega_2) = 2H_I(j\omega_1^{\,O}, j\omega_2^{\,E}) = 0 \qquad (2.117)$$

From symmetry,

$$H_I(j\omega_1^{\,E}, j\omega_2^{\,O}) = 0 \qquad (2.118)$$

Equations 2.116, 2.117, 2.118, and 2.86 imply that $H_R(j\omega_1^{\,E}, j\omega_2^{\,E})$ = an arbitrary constant, which is a separable kernel. Thus there is a contradiction, and the statement is proved.

Therefore, for nonseparable systems, we can use Equation 2.107 directly. For separable systems, Equation 2.107 gives half of $\Theta(\omega_1, \omega_2)$. The other half is obtained from symmetry.

The phase functions that we obtain are clearly not unique. We can show, however, that they are the minimum-phase networks associated with the given gain characteristic.

To prove the minimum-phase property, we have to show that any other realizable system with the same gain function takes on a zero value somewhere in the half planes belonging to $\sigma_1 > 0$ and $\sigma_2 > 0$. Then we must show that this implies that the second function accumulates phase shift faster for any path in the ω_1, ω_2 plane.

Let the original minimum-phase function be $K_m(j\omega_1, j\omega_2)$. Consider a new function

$$H(j\omega_1, j\omega_2) = K_M(j\omega_1, j\omega_2) \cdot \frac{A(j\omega_1, j\omega_2)}{B(j\omega_1, j\omega_2)} \qquad (2.119)$$

with the constraint

$$|H(j\omega_1, j\omega_2)| = |K_M(j\omega_1, j\omega_2)| \qquad (2.120)$$

This implies that

$$\left|\frac{A(j\omega_1, j\omega_2)}{B(j\omega_1, j\omega_2)}\right|^2 = \frac{A(j\omega_1, j\omega_2)}{B(j\omega_1, j\omega_2)} \cdot \frac{A(-j\omega_1, -j\omega_2)}{B(-j\omega_1, -j\omega_2)} = 1 \qquad (2.121)$$

We obtain

$$\frac{A(j\omega_1, j\omega_2)}{B(j\omega_1, j\omega_2)} = \frac{B(-j\omega_1, -j\omega_2)}{A(-j\omega_1, -j\omega_2)} \qquad (2.122)$$

Letting $s_1 = j\omega_1$ and $s_2 = j\omega_2$, we can write

$$\frac{A(s_1, s_2)}{B(s_1, s_2)} = \frac{B(-s_1, -s_2)}{A(-s_1, -s_2)} \qquad (2.123)$$

Equation 2.123 implies that

$$A(s_1, s_2) = B(-s_1, -s_2) \tag{2.124}$$

Now consider the class of rational transforms. We can write

$$A(s_1, s_2) = a_{00} + a_{10}s_1 + a_{01}s_2 + a_{20}s_1^2 + a_{11}s_1s_2 + a_{02}s_2^2 + a_{30}s_1^3$$
$$+ a_{21}s_1^2s_2 + a_{12}s_1s_2^2 + a_{03}s_2^3 + \ldots + a_{0n}s_2^n \tag{2.125}$$

$$B(s_1, s_2) = b_{00} + b_{10}s_1 + b_{01}s_2 + b_{20}s_1^2 + b_{11}s_1s_2 + b_{02}s_2^2 + b_{30}s_1^3$$
$$+ b_{21}s_1^2s_2 + b_{12}s_1s_2^2 + b_{03}s_2^3 + \ldots + b_{0n}s_2^n \tag{2.126}$$

Using Equation 2.124, we can write the phase function in the following form:

$$\Theta(j\omega_1, j\omega_2) = \tan^{-1}\left(\frac{-b_{10}\omega_1 - b_{01}\omega_2 + b_{30}\omega_1^3 + b_{21}\omega_1^2\omega_2 + \ldots}{b_{00} - b_{20}\omega_1^2 - b_{11}\omega_1\omega_2 - b_{02}\omega_2^2 + \ldots}\right)$$
$$-\tan^{-1}\left(\frac{+b_{10}\omega_1 + b_{01}\omega_2 - b_{30}\omega_1^3 - b_{21}\omega_1^2\omega_2 + \ldots}{b_{00} - b_{20}\omega_1^2 - b_{11}\omega_1\omega_2 - b_{02}\omega_2^2 + \ldots}\right) \tag{2.127}$$

We wish to show that $\Theta(j\omega_1, j\omega_2)$ is a decreasing function of ω_1 and ω_2. Consider now the ω_1, ω_2 plane shown in Figure 2.13. We want to examine an arbitrary path subject to the restriction that both ω_1 and ω_2 are either increasing or constant along the path.

For any arbitrary path we can write $\omega_2 = g(\omega_1)$. The only exceptions are segments with $\omega_2 = k_0$ that can be treated separately.

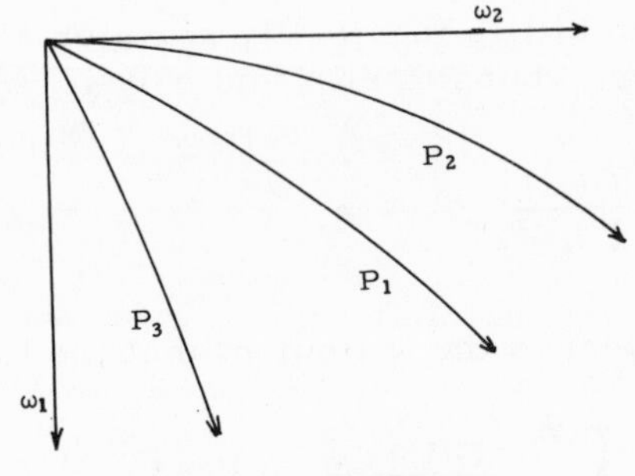

Figure 2.13. Possible paths in ω_1 - ω_2 plane

Therefore we can write the all-pass part of our transforms as

$$\frac{A(s_1, s_2)}{B(s_1, s_2)} = \frac{A(s_1, jg(\omega_1))}{B(s_1, jg(\omega_1))} = \frac{A^*(s_1)}{B^*(s_1)} \tag{2.128}$$

which is just a one-dimensional transform with $A^*(s_1) = B^*(-s_1)$. If we can show that the system is stable for any $g(\omega_1)$, then the one-dimensional pole-zero plot will be of the form shown in Figure 2.14. Clearly, this has a nonincreasing phase function.

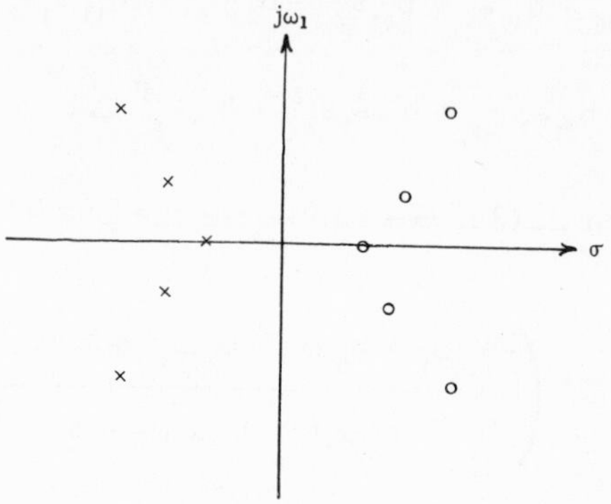

Figure 2.14. One-dimensional pole-zero plot

We shall show in the next section that the stability of $B(s_1, s_2)$ implies the stability of $B^*(s_1)$. Since $\frac{1}{K_M(s_1, s_2)}$ is realizable and stable, it is necessary that $B(s_1, s_2)$ be stable in order for the over-all system $H(s_1, s_2)$ defined in Equation 2.119 to be stable. Therefore we can conclude that our kernel is a minimum-phase kernel.

For one-dimensional transforms, the Paley-Wiener criterion gives necessary and sufficient conditions for a function $G(j\omega)$ to be the gain function of a realizable system. If $G(j\omega)$ is defined as $\log|H(j\omega)|$, then $h(t)$ is identically zero for all $t < -t_0$ (t_0 is arbitrarily large, but finite) if and only if

$$\int_{-\infty}^{\infty} \frac{G(j\omega)}{1+\omega^2}\, d\omega < \infty \tag{2.129}$$

This is equivalent to the statement that the Hilbert transform

$$-\frac{1}{\pi}\int_{-\infty}^{\infty} \frac{G(j\omega)}{\omega_1 - \omega}\, d\omega = \Theta(j\omega) \tag{2.130}$$

exists if and only if Equation 2. 129 is satisfied.

As shown in Equation 2. 107, we obtain $G(\omega_1, \omega_2)$ by a single integration:

$$\Theta(j\omega_1, j\omega_2) = -\frac{1}{\pi}\int_{-\infty}^{\infty} \frac{G(j\omega_3, j\omega_2)}{\omega_1 - \omega_3}\, d\omega_3 \qquad (2.\ 107)$$

Therefore the integral in Equation 2. 107 will exist if and only if

$$\int_{-\infty}^{\infty} \frac{|G(j\omega_1, j\omega_2)}{1+\omega_1^2}\, d\omega_1 < \infty \qquad \text{for all } \omega_2 \qquad (2.\ 131)$$

Thus the Paley-Wiener criterion can be extended to determine the realizability of any n^{th}-order gain function.

Stability of nth-Order Kernels. We should like to investigate the stability of the transform defined in Equation 2. 60:

$$K_2(s_1, s_2) = \int_{\sigma_1 - j\infty}^{\sigma_1 + j\infty} \int_{\sigma_2 - j\infty}^{\sigma_2 + j\infty} k_2(t_1, t_2)\, e^{-s_1 t_1} e^{-s_2 t_2}\, dt_1\, dt_2 \qquad (2.\ 60)$$

First, assume that $k_2(t_1, t_2)$ is realizable.† For $k(t_1, t_2)$ to be a stable impulse response, it is necessary and sufficient for the integral to converge for all $\sigma_1 : 0 \le \sigma_1 < \infty$ and $\sigma_2 : 0 \le \sigma_2 < \infty$. For rational transfer functions, a generalized Routh criterion may be used.

Consider the denominator of Equation 2. 62. Instead of writing it as a double sum, we shall construct a simple array of the coefficients as follows:

		s_2	s_2^2	s_2^3	s_2^4
	a_{00}	a_{01}	a_{02}	a_{03}	
s_1	a_{10}	a_{11}	a_{12}		
s_1^2	a_{20}	a_{21}			
s_1^3	a_{30}				
s_1^4					

† Clearly, this means that the region of convergence may no longer include the $j\omega_1$ and $j\omega_2$ axes.

First, we can apply the Routh test to a polynomial in s_1:

$$P(s_1) = A + Bs_1 + Cs_1^2 + Ds_1^3 \tag{2.132}$$

where

$$A = \sum_{i=0}^{3} a_{0i} s_2^i, \quad B = \sum_{i=0}^{2} s_{1i} s_2^i, \quad C = \sum_{i=0}^{1} a_{2i} s_2^i, \quad D = a_{30}$$

The requirements for stability are

$$A, B, C > 0, \; D \geq 0, \; BC - DA > 0 \tag{2.133}$$

Since A, B, and C are functions of s_2, we have to satisfy the inequalities in Equation 2.133 for all $s_2 : 0 \leq \sigma_2 < \infty$.

Assume that $a_{00} > 0$. Then $A > 0$ for all s_2; and $0 \leq \sigma_2 < \infty$ is simply the requirement that

$$A = a_{00} + a_{01}s_2 + a_{02}s_2^2 + a_{03}s_2^3 = 0 \tag{2.134}$$

has no roots with positive real parts. Use of the Routh criterion gives the requirements

$$a_{03} \geq 0; \; a_{02}, a_{01}, a_{00} > 0; \; a_{02}a_{00} > a_{03}a_{01} \tag{2.135}$$

Similarly, $B > 0$ requires that

$$a_{10}, a_{11} > 0; \; a_{12} \geq 0 \tag{2.136}$$

and $C > 0$, $D > 0$ requires that

$$a_{20} > 0; \; a_{21} \geq 0; \; a_{30} \geq 0 \tag{2.137}$$

The inequality $BC - DA > 0$ requires that

$$(a_{10} + a_{11}s_2 + a_{12}s_2^2)(a_{20} + a_{21}s_2) - a_{30}(a_{00} + a_{01}s_2 + a_{02}s_2^2 + a_{03}s_2^3) > 0 \tag{2.138}$$

has no roots with positive real parts. This implies the following inequalities:

$$a_{12}a_{21} - a_{30}a_{03} \geq 0; \; a_{11}a_{21} + a_{20}a_{12} - a_{30}a_{02} \geq 0;$$

$$a_{10}a_{21} + a_{11}a_{20} - a_{30}a_{01} > 0; \; a_{10}a_{20} - a_{30}a_{00} > 0 \text{ and}$$

$$(a_{11}a_{21} + a_{20}a_{12} - a_{30}a_{02})(a_{10}a_{21} + a_{11}a_{20} - a_{30}a_{01})$$

$$- (a_{12}a_{21} - a_{30}a_{03})(a_{10}a_{20} - a_{30}a_{00}) > 0 \tag{2.139}$$

The inequalities in 2.133 through 2.139 must be satisfied for the transform to represent a realizable and stable impulse response.

The extension to n dimensions requires increasing the dimension of the array. The Routh criterion is applied in succession to each dimension.

A simple example of a stable filter kernel is

$$H(s_1, s_2) = \frac{s_1 + s_2 + 2a}{(s_1 + s_2 + a)(s_1 + a)(s_2 + a)} \qquad (2.140)$$

The array of the denominator is

		s_2	s_2^2
	a^3	$2a^2$	
s_1	$2a$	$3a$	1
s_1^2	a	1	

Clearly, $a > 0$ ensures stability. Here the transform represents the cascade shown in Figure 2.15.

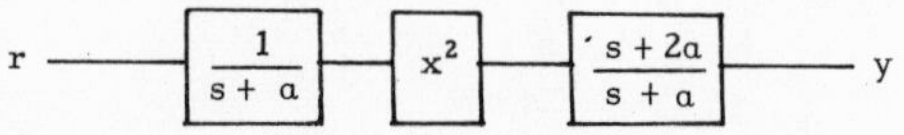

Figure 2.15. Stable second-order system

An example of an unstable kernel is

$$H(s_1, s_2) = \frac{1}{-s_2^2 + (a + s_1)^2} \qquad \begin{Bmatrix} +a < \mathrm{Re}(s_1) \\ +a < \mathrm{Re}(s_2) \end{Bmatrix} \qquad (2.141)$$

The unsymmetrized array is

		s_2	s_2^2
	a^2	0	-1
s_1	$2a$		
s_2	1		

which does not satisfy the criterion of this section. The

symmetrical impulse response corresponding to Equation 2.141 is

$$h_2(t_1, t_2) = u_{-1}(t_1)\, e^{-at_1}\, u_0(t_1 - t_2) + u_{-1}(t_1)\, e^{+at_1}\, u_0(t_1 - t_2) \qquad (2.142)$$

The corresponding system is shown in Figure 2.16.

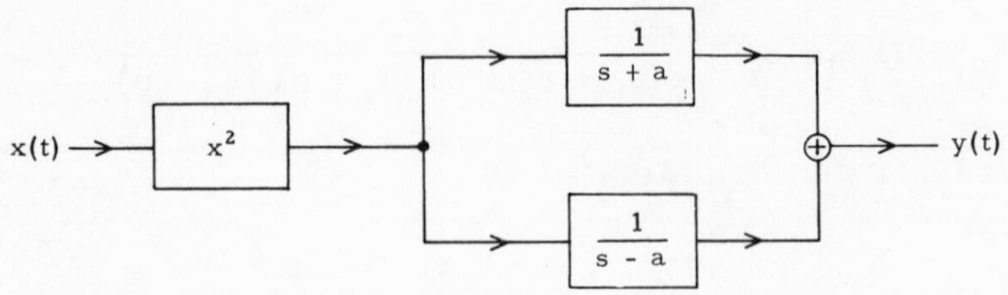

Figure 2.16. An unstable system

We have now developed the properties that transforms for stable n^{th}-order impulse responses must have. These properties form a useful foundation for the nonlinear synthesis problem. In our case, they assure us that the nonlinear filter which we are trying to simulate with a control system is realizable and stable. With these properties for a background, we shall return to our main problem.

Chapter 3

FUNCTIONAL POWER SERIES COMPENSATION SOLUTION

1. General Approach

We now wish to apply the functional method of characterization to the solution of the compensation problem.

The general configuration of the feedback control system was shown in Figure 1.2. Let us consider two important special cases of this general configuration. For $C_b = 1$, we have the "series compensation" problem (Figure 3.1). For $C_a = 1$, we

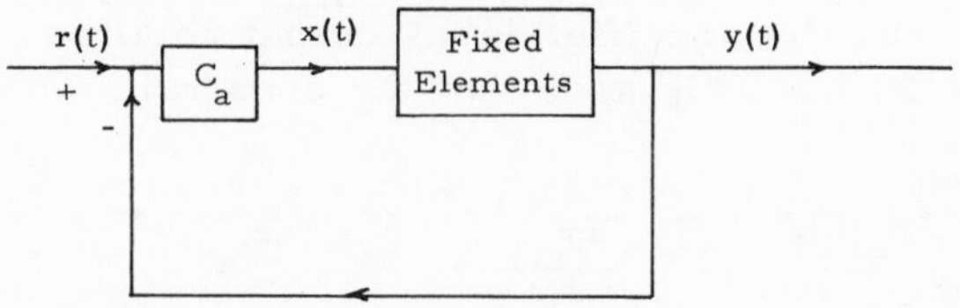

Figure 3.1. Series compensation configuration

have the "feedback compensation" problem (Figure 3.2). In many cases the proper choice of configuration will be obvious. We shall see that our solution will be convergent within certain bounds on the input magnitude r(t). By judiciously choosing either C_a or C_b, we can improve this bound. In some cases, a convergent solution can be obtained by using both C_a and C_b when neither one alone would be satisfactory.

The optimum nonlinear filter is specified by a set of Volterra kernels, $K_1, K_2, \ldots, K_N$. In general, this set will be finite because the statistics are limited. This set of kernels will be referred to as the filter kernels.

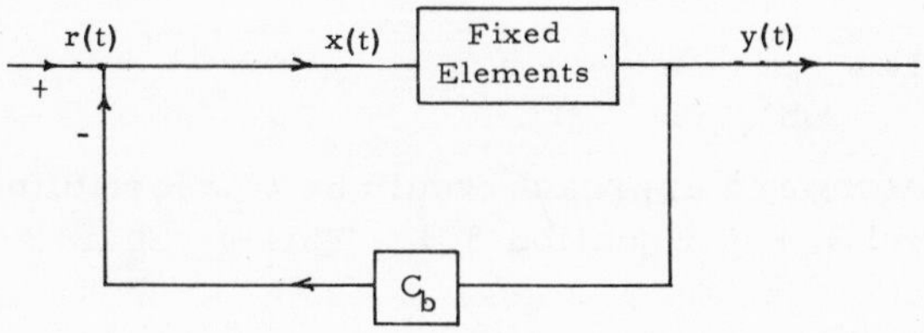

Figure 3.2. Feedback compensation configuration

The basic equations describing the system in Figure 3. 1 are

$$P_1(x, \dot{x}, \ddot{x}, \ldots, x^{(r)}) = P_2(y, \dot{y}, \ddot{y}, \ldots, y^{(s)}) \qquad (3.1)$$

$$x(t) = \int_{-\infty}^{\infty} C_1(t - \tau)\, e(\tau)\, d\tau$$

$$+ \int_{-\infty}^{\infty}\int_{-\infty}^{\infty} C_2(t - \tau_1, t - \tau_2)\, e(\tau_1)\, e(\tau_2)\, d\tau_1\, d\tau_2 + \ldots ^{\dagger} \qquad (3.2)$$

$$e(t) = r(t) - y(t) \qquad (3.3)$$

We want to find a set of kernels $C_1, \ldots, C_k$ so that the overall system has the specified input-output relation. Therefore we choose $C_1, \ldots, C_k$ such that the constraint equation†

$$y(t) = \int_{-\infty}^{\infty} K_1(t - \tau)\, r(\tau)\, d\tau$$

$$+ \int_{-\infty}^{\infty}\int_{-\infty}^{\infty} K_2(t - \tau_1, t - \tau_2)\, r(\tau_1)\, r(\tau_2)\, d\tau_1\, d\tau_2 + \ldots \qquad (3.4)$$

is satisfied.

As an example, let us consider a specific set of fixed elements described by the differential equation

$$\ddot{y} + a\dot{y} + b = x + dx^3 \qquad (3.5)$$

or

$$L[y] = x + dx^3 \qquad (3.6)$$

where L is the linear operator defined by

$$L \equiv \frac{d^2}{dt^2} + a\frac{d}{dt} + b \qquad (3.7)$$

A straightforward approach would be to substitute Equations 3. 2, 3. 3, and 3. 4 in Equation 3. 1. This gives an equation of the form

---

† Later we shall introduce a more compact notation to represent the functional series. Then Equation 3. 2 will be

$$x = \underline{C}[e]$$

$$L\left[\int_{-\infty}^{\infty} K_1(t-\tau)\,r(\tau)\,d\tau + \int_{-\infty}^{\infty}\int_{-\infty}^{\infty} K_2(t-\tau_1, t-\tau_2)\,r(\tau_1)\,r(\tau_2)\,d\tau_1\,d\tau_2 + \dots\right]$$

$$= \Bigg\{\int_{-\infty}^{\infty} C_1(t-\tau)\left[r(\tau) - \int_{-\infty}^{\infty} K_1(\tau-\epsilon)\,r(\epsilon)\,d\epsilon\right.$$

$$\left. - \int_{-\infty}^{\infty}\int_{-\infty}^{\infty} K_2(\tau-\epsilon_1, \tau-\epsilon_2)\,r(\tau_1)\,r(\tau_2)\,d\tau_1\,d\tau_2 + \dots\right]$$

$$+ \int_{-\infty}^{\infty}\int_{-\infty}^{\infty} d\tau_1\,d\tau_2\,C_2(t-\tau_1, t-\tau_2)\left[r(\tau_1) - \int_{-\infty}^{\infty} K_1(\tau_1-\epsilon)\,r(\epsilon)\,d\epsilon + \dots\right]$$

$$\times\left[r(\tau_2) - \int_{-\infty}^{\infty} K_1(\tau_2-\epsilon)\,r(\epsilon)\,d\epsilon + \dots\right]$$

$$+ \int_{-\infty}^{\infty}\int_{-\infty}^{\infty}\int_{-\infty}^{\infty} d\tau_1\,d\tau_2\,d\tau_3\,C_3(t-\tau_1, t-\tau_2, t-\tau_3)$$

$$\times\left[r(\tau_1) - \int_{-\infty}^{\infty} K_1(\tau_1-\epsilon)\,r(\epsilon)\,d\epsilon + \dots\right]$$

$$\times\left[r(\tau_2) - \int_{-\infty}^{\infty} K_1(\tau_2-\epsilon)\,r(\epsilon)\,d\epsilon + \dots\right]\left[r(\tau_3) - \int_{-\infty}^{\infty} K_1(\tau_3-\epsilon)\,r(\epsilon)\,d\epsilon + \dots\right]\Bigg\}$$

$$+ d\Bigg\{\left[\int_{-\infty}^{\infty} C_1(t-\tau)\left[r(\tau) - \int_{-\infty}^{\infty} K_1(\tau-\epsilon)\,d\epsilon + \dots\right] d\tau\right]^3$$

$$+ 3\left[\int_{-\infty}^{\infty} d\tau\,C_1(t-\tau)\left[r(\tau) - \int_{-\infty}^{\infty} K_1(\tau-\epsilon)\,r(\epsilon)\,d\epsilon + \dots\right]\right]^2$$

$$\times\left[\int_{-\infty}^{\infty} d\tau_1\,d\tau_2\,C_2(t-\tau_1, t-\tau_2)\left[r(\tau_1) - \int_{-\infty}^{\infty} K_1(\tau_1-\epsilon)\,r(\epsilon)\,d\epsilon - \dots\right]\right.$$

$$\left.\times\left[r(\tau_2) - \int_{-\infty}^{\infty} K_1(\tau_2-\epsilon)\,r(\epsilon)\,d\epsilon + \dots\right]\right] + \dots\Bigg\} \qquad (3.8)$$

By equating terms of the same order in r(t), a set of equations can be obtained which can be solved successively, not simultaneously, for the various C_m. The easiest approach to solving these equations is through multidimensional transform theory. Even with the use of transforms, a straightforward approach turns out to be too tedious to be useful as a general method. In order to motivate the algorithm that we are going to develop, we shall solve for the first few terms directly.

Applying the transform properties developed in the previous chapter to the basic equations of the system, we can write the equations for the lower-order kernels rather easily. Letting the transform of the linear operator $L = G_y(s)$. we have

$$C_1(s)\,[1 - K_1(s)]\,R(s) = G_y(s)\,K_1(s)\,R(s) \tag{3.9}$$

$$-C_1(s_1 + s_2)\,K_2(s_1, s_2)\,R(s_1)\,R(s_2) + C_2(s_1, s_2)\prod_{i=1}^{2}[1 - K_1(s_1)]\,R(s_1)\,R(s$$

$$= G_y(s_1 + s_2)\,K_2(s_1, s_2)\,R(s_1)\,R(s_2) \tag{3.10}$$

$$-C_1(s_1 + s_2 + s_3)\,K_3(s_1, s_2, s_3)\,R(s_1)\,R(s_2)\,R(s_3)$$

$$+ 2C_2(s_1 + s_2 + s_3)\,[1 - K_1(s_i)]\,K_2(s_2, s_3)\,R(s_1)\,R(s_2)\,R(s_3)$$

$$+ C_3(s_1, s_2, s_3)\left[\prod_{i=1}^{3}[1 - K_1(s_i)]\right]R(s_1)\,R(s_2)\,R(s_3)$$

$$+ d\prod_{i=1}^{3} C_1(s_i)\,[1 - K_1(s_i)]$$

$$= G_y(s_1 + s_2 + s_3)\,K_3(s_1, s_2, s_3)\,R(s_1)\,R(s_2)\,R(s_3) \tag{3.11}$$

We observe that the only unknown in the first equation is $C_1(s)$. Solving, we get

$$C_1(s) = \frac{G_y(s)\,K_1(s)}{1 - K_1(s)} \tag{3.12}$$

We can see that the first-order compensator kernel depends

only on the linear part of the fixed elements and the first-order filter kernel. Let us look at Equations 3.9 and 3.10 and observe where each of the terms originate.

Thus in Equation 3.9 the term $C_1(s)[1 - K_1(s)]\, R(s)$ results from the linear input term. Let us label this term $P_1^{\,1}$. The superscript denotes the order of input variable which contributed the term, and the subscript denotes the C_m for which we are solving. The term $G(s)\, K_1(s)\, R(s)$ is due to the linear output term and can be labeled $Q_1^{\,1}$. In Equation 3.10, we see that the term

$$\left\{ - C_1(s_1 + s_2)\, K_2(s_1, s_2)\, R(s_1)\, R(s_2) + C_2(s_1, s_2) \left[\prod_{i=1}^{2} [1 - K_1(s_i)] \right] R(s_1)\, R(s_2) \right\}$$

is caused by the linear input term and can be labeled $P_2^{\,1}$. Similarly, we see that the mth equation has terms contributed by all terms in the differential equation whose order is less than or equal to m. The terms contain only filter kernels of order less than or equal to m. We also note that the only unknown quantity in the mth equation is the kernel C_m. Thus we realize that by using a set of compensator kernels C_1 through C_m, we can satisfy the constraint equation through the mth term. Equations 3.9, 3.10, and 3.11 can be solved successively, not simultaneously, to give the required C_m. Trying to write the equations for m = 4 and 5, however, convinces us of the necessity for a more efficient approach. An algorithm can be developed that enables us to write efficiently the mth equation.

2. Algorithm for Determining Series Compensator Kernels

The input-output relation of the fixed elements is described by a nonlinear differential equation. We observed that the equation in which a contribution from a given term first appeared was determined by the order of the nonlinearity. First, then, we will classify the terms according to the order of their nonlinearity.

Thus x^3, $\dot{x}(\ddot{x})^2$, $x\dot{x}\ddot{x}$ are all third-order input terms. There is a basic expansion for all n^{th}-order terms. The algorithm developed enables us to write an equation for C_m in the transform domain by considering the expansion of the nth-order terms directly. Consider the equation

$$ay^2\dot{y} + by^3 + cy^2 + d(\dot{y})^2 + L(y) = L(x) + ex^3 + f\dot{x}(\ddot{x})^2 + gx\dot{x}\ddot{x} \tag{3.13}$$

In order to solve for the mth-order compensator kernel C_m, we can write an equation of the form

$$Q_m^{\,3} + Q_m^{\,2} + Q_m^{\,1} = P_m^{\,1} + P_m^{\,3} \tag{3.14}$$

where Q_m^3 represents the contribution of all third-order output terms, P_m^1 represents the contribution of all linear input terms, and the other terms have similar definitions, as explained above. The transform of the unknown kernel appears in P_m^1. All other quantities are known, so that the explicit answer follows immediately.

We shall see that the basic expansion for all n^{th}-order terms is a combination of different partitions. The difference between terms within a given order is taken into account by use of a characteristic coefficient that modifies the basic expansion.

Therefore the only problem is to find an efficient method for constructing the terms P_m^n and Q_m^n.

First, we shall develop the construction of P_m^n. As defined above, P_m^n is the contribution of an nth-order nonlinearity in the input to the fixed elements to an mth-order compensator kernel. Also, P_m^n consists of a sum of $m - n + 1$ terms. Thus we may write

$$P_m^n = \sum_{i=n}^{m} P_m^n(i) \tag{3.15}$$

and determine each $P_m^n(i)$. We can construct $P_m^n(i)$ in three steps.

First, form all partitions of m objects into n cells. For example, the partitions for $m = 7$ and $n = 3$ are

1	1	5

p_{115}

1	2	4

p_{124}

1	3	3

p_{133}

2	2	3

p_{233}

These are the basic or major partitions. Physically, each object represents a different frequency-domain variable.

Second, consider all combinations of n compensator kernels C_j, where $\Sigma j = i$. For $i = 5$ and $n = 3$, the possible combinations are C_1, C_2, C_2 and C_1, C_1, C_3. Compare each set of kernels with each major partition in turn. Looking at p_{115} and C_1, C_2, C_2 first, we see that they cannot occur together. The C_2 represents a kernel that is a function of at least two variables, $C_2(s_1, s_2)$. But two of the partitions in p_{115} have only one variable in them. Thus we cannot associate C_1, C_2, C_2 and p_{115}. Examples of correct associations are

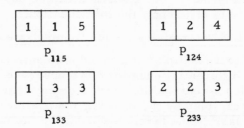

(Ia)

1	1	5
C_1	C_1	C_3

(IIa)

1	2	4
C_1	C_2	C_2

Third, look at the ways in which the optimum filter kernels K_β can combine with the compensator kernels C_j. Here the necessary restriction is that $\Sigma\beta = m$ and that the total number of kernels $K_\beta = i$. For partition Ia, we see that suitable combinations are

<table>
<tr><td>1</td><td>1</td><td colspan="3">5</td></tr>
<tr><td>C_1</td><td>C_1</td><td colspan="3">C_3</td></tr>
<tr><td>K_1</td><td>K_1</td><td>K_1</td><td>K_1</td><td>K_3</td></tr>
</table>

or

<table>
<tr><td>1</td><td>1</td><td colspan="3">5</td></tr>
<tr><td>C_1</td><td>C_1</td><td colspan="3">C_3</td></tr>
<tr><td>K_1</td><td>K_1</td><td>K_1</td><td>K_2</td><td>K_2</td></tr>
</table>

These represent the transformed terms

$$[C_1(s_1)\ (1 - K_1(s_1))]\ [C_1(s_2)\ (1 - K_1(s_2))]$$

$$\times\ [C_3(s_3,\ s_4,\ s_5 + s_6 + s_7)\ (1 - K_1(s_3))\ (1 - K_1(s_4))\ K_3(s_5,\ s_6,\ s_7)]$$

and

$$[C_1(s_1)\ (1 - K_1(s_1))]\ [C_1(s_2)\ (1 - K_1(s_2))]$$

$$\times\ [C_3(s_3,\ s_4 + s_5,\ s_6 + s_7)\ (1 - K_1(s_3))\ K_2(s_4,\ s_5)\ K_2(s_6,\ s_7)]$$

To complete $P_7{}^3(5)$, consider the remaining partitions and the kernels associated with them. In tabular form, the complete process and results are

$P_7{}^3(5)$:

p_{115} →

<table>
<tr><td>1</td><td>1</td><td colspan="3">5</td></tr>
<tr><td>C_1</td><td>C_1</td><td colspan="3">C_3</td></tr>
<tr><td>K_1</td><td>K_1</td><td>K_1</td><td>K_1</td><td>K_3</td></tr>
<tr><td>C_1</td><td>C_1</td><td colspan="3">C_3</td></tr>
<tr><td>K_1</td><td>K_1</td><td>K_1</td><td>K_2</td><td>K_2</td></tr>
</table>

$$\rightarrow C_1(s_1)\,C_1(s_2)\,C_3(s_3,\ s_4,\ s_5 + s_6 + s_7) \times \prod_{i=1}^{4} [1 - K_1(s_i)]\ K_3(s_5,\ s_6,\ s_7)$$

$$\rightarrow C_1(s_1)\,C_1(s_2)\,C_3(s_3,\ s_4 + s_5,\ s_6 + s_7) \times \prod_{i=1}^{3} [1 - K_1(s_i)]\ K_2(s_4,\ s_5)\,K_2(s_6,\ s_7)$$

$p_{124} \rightarrow$

1	2	4		
C_1	C_1	C_3		
K_1	K_2	K_1	K_1	K_1
C_1	C_2	C_2		
K_1	K_1K_1	K_1	K_3	
C_1	C_2	C_2		
K_1	K_1K_1	K_2	K_2	

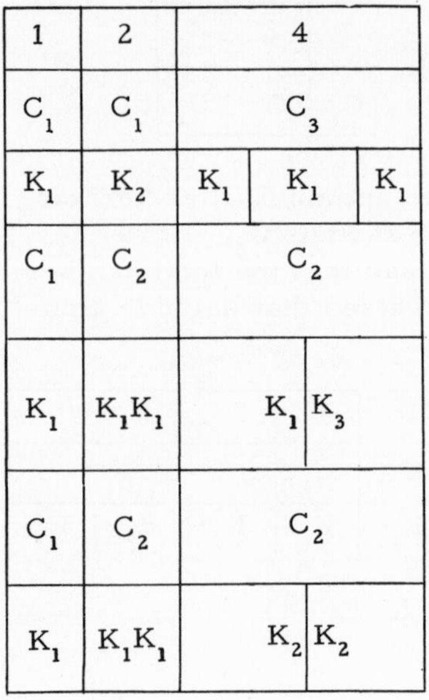

$$\rightarrow C_1(s_1)\, C_1(s_2 + s_3)\, C_3(s_4, s_5, s_6 + s_7) \times [1 - K_1(s_1)]\, K_2(s_2, s_3)\, [1 - K_1(s_4)] \times [1 - K_1(s_5)]\, K_2(s_6, s_7)$$

$$\rightarrow C_1(s_1)\, C_2(s_2, s_3)\, C_2(s_4, s_5, s_6 + s_7) \times \prod_{i=1}^{4} [1 - K_1(s_i)]\, K_3(s_5, s_6, s_7)$$

$$\rightarrow C_1(s_1)\, C_2(s_2, s_3)\, C_2(s_4 + s_5, s_6 + s_7) \times \prod_{i=1}^{3} [1 - K_1(s_i)]\, K_2(s_4, s_5)\, K_2(s_6, s_7$$

$p_{133} \rightarrow$

1	3	3		
C_1	C_1	C_3		
K_1	K_3	K_1	K_1	K_1
C_1	C_2	C_2		
K_1	K_1K_2	K_1	K_2	

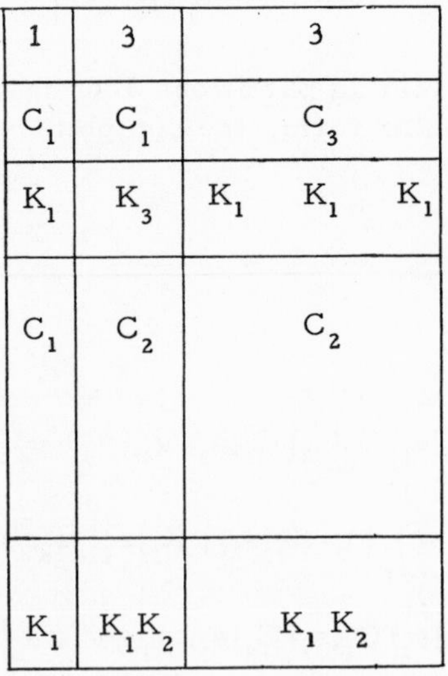

$$\rightarrow C_1(s_1)\, C_1(s_2 + s_3 + s_4)\, C_3(s_5, s_6, s_7) \times [1 - K_1(s_1)]\, K_3(s_2, s_3, s_4) \times \prod_{i=5}^{7} [1 - K_1(s_i)]$$

$$\rightarrow C_1(s_1)\, C_2(s_2, s_3 + s_4)\, C_2(s_5, s_6 + s_7) \times \prod_{i=1,2,5} [1 - K_1(s_i)]\, K_2(s_3, s_4)\, K_2(s_6,$$

p_{223} →	2	2	3
	C_1	C_2	C_2
	K_2	K_1K_1	K_1K_2
	C_2	C_2	C_1
	K_1K_1	K_1K_1	K_3
	C_1	C_1	C_3
	K_2	K_2	$K_1K_1K_1$

$$\rightarrow C_1(s_1 + s_2)\, C_2(s_3, s_4)\, C_2(s_5, s_6 + s_7) \times K_2(s_1, s_2) \prod_{i=3,4,5} [1 = K_1(s_i)]\, K_2(s_6, s_7)$$

$$\rightarrow C_2(s_1, s_2)\, C_2(s_3, s_4)\, C_1(s_5 + s_6 + s_7) \times \prod_{i=1}^{4} [1 - K_1(s_i)]\, K_3(s_5, s_6, s_7)$$

$$\rightarrow C_1(s_1 + s_2)\, C_1(s_3 + s_4)\, C_3(s_5, s_6, s_7) \times K_2(s_1, s_2)\, K_2(s_3, s_4) \prod_{i=5}^{7} [1 - K_1(s_i)]$$

There are three quantities that remain to be specified: the sign of each p, the numerical coefficient of each p, and the characteristic coefficient associated with each p.

(a) The sign of each p equals $(-1)^r$, where r is defined as the number of kernels K with a subscript other than 1.

(b) The numerical coefficient is determined by two multiplicative factors. The first factor is equal to the number of distinct arrangements that are possible by changing the ordering within the various subpartitions. (A subpartition is the partition within a specific compensator kernel.) The second factor comes from the rearrangement of the various compensator kernels in all possible distinct ways. This factor is simply equal to the number of permutations of n objects. Kernels with the same subscript and the same number of variables are considered identical in this permutation.

(c) The characteristic coefficient is a function only of the index of p and not of the particular kernel it represents. For instance, the characteristic coefficient of $\ddot{x}\dot{x}x$ pertaining to p_{115} is

$$\frac{1}{3}\left[s_1^{\,2} s_2^{\,1} \cdot \left(\sum_{i=3}^{7} s_i\right)^{0} + s_2^{\,2} \cdot \left(\sum_{i=3}^{7} s_i\right)^{1} \cdot s_1^{\,0} + \left(\sum_{i=3}^{7} s_i\right)^{2} s_1^{\,1} s_2^{\,0} \right]$$

which reduces to

$$\frac{1}{3}\left[s_1^{\,2}\, s_2 + s_2^{\,2} \left(\sum_{i=3}^{7} s_i \right) + \left(\sum_{i=3}^{7} s_i \right)^{2} s_1 \right]$$

This comes from the general rule of writing the variables as a product of a summation of s's. The number of s's in each sum is equal to the argument of the p function. The exponent to which each sum is raised is equal to the order of the respective derivative. The terms are then permuted. Clearly, for a term containing no derivatives, the characteristic coefficient is simply 1.

As an example, consider a typical term of $P_7^{\,3}(5)$ with respect to the fixed elements described by Equation 3.5:

$p''_{124} =$

1	2	4
C_1	C_2	C_2
K_1	K_1K_1	K_1K_3

$$\rightarrow C_1(s_1)\, C_2(s_2, s_3)\, C_2(s_4, s_5 + s_6 + s_7) \times \prod_{i=1}^{4} [1 - K_1(s_i)]\, K_3(s_5, s_6, s_7)$$

(a) Since r = 1, the sign is $(-1)^1 = -1$.

(b) The first factor of the numerical coefficient is 2. This comes from rearranging the subpartition corresponding to $C_2(s_4, s_5 + s_6 + s_7)$. The second factor is 3.

(c) The characteristic coefficient is 1 because there are no derivatives. The complete term is

$$-6\, C_1(s_1)\, C_2(s_2, s_3)\, C_2(s_4, s_5 + s_6 + s_7) \prod_{i=1}^{4} [1 - K_1(s_i)]\, K_3(s_5, s_6, s_7$$

As one would expect, the compensator term is rather complicated. When we look at the examples and means of synthesis, however, we shall see that the kernels are built up by combinations of smaller, less formidable systems.

Now examine the construction of $Q_m^{\,n}$. The term $Q_m^{\,n}$ is the contribution of an nth-order nonlinearity of the output to an mth-order series compensator kernel. The nonlinear output terms are subject to similar, although simpler, expansion rules. By looking at the original equations, we see that

$$y(t)^n = \left[\int_{-\infty}^{\infty} K_1(t-\tau)\, r(\tau)\, d\tau \right.$$

$$\left. + \int_{-\infty}^{\infty}\int_{-\infty}^{\infty} K_2(t-\tau_1,\ t-\tau_2)\, r(\tau_1)\, r(\tau_2)\, d\tau_1\, d\tau_2 + \dots \right]^n$$

Therefore, to find $Q_m^{\ n}$, we construct all possible partitions of m objects into n cells. For example, let $n = 3$ and $m = 5$. Possible partitions are

1	1	3

q_{113}

1	2	2

q_{122}

which represent $K_1(s_1)\, K_1(s_2)\, K_3(s_3,\ s_4,\ s_5)$ and $K_1(s_1)\, K_2(s_2,\ s_3)$ $K_2(s_4,\ s_5)$, respectively.

The sign of each term is positive. The numerical coefficient is equal to the number of different ways in which the partition can be ordered. The characteristic coefficient is determined in exactly the same manner as it was for an input term.†

To demonstrate the application of the algorithm, an example will be given. This example is reasonably simple, so that the technique will not be obscured by too much detail.

Consider a system whose fixed elements are described by

$$cx + dx^3 = \ddot{y} + a\dot{y} + by \tag{3.16}$$

The desired operation of the over-all system is represented by a linear kernel K_1. The system is of the form shown in Figure 3.1.

We can write the linear term by inspection and then use the algorithm to find the higher-order kernels:

$$(s^2 + as + b)\, K_1(s) = cC_1(s_1)\, [1 - K_1(s)] \tag{3.17}$$

This yields

$$C_1(s) = \frac{1}{c}\ \frac{(s^2 + as + b)\, K_1(s)}{1 - K_1(s)} \tag{3.18}$$

---

† One observes that in order to find the functional representation corresponding to a given differential equation, one can apply the $Q_m^{\ n}$ algorithm to both sides of the differential equation.

The next nonzero equation is for C_3:

(a) Since $K_n = 0$ for $n \neq 1$, $Q_3^{\,1} = 0$.
(b) We find that $P_3^{\,1} = P_3^{\,1}(1) + P_3^{\,1}(2) + P_3^{\,1}(3)$.

For $P_3^{\,1}(1)$:

3
C_1
K_3

$\rightarrow 0$ since $K_3 = 0$

For $P_3^{\,1}(2)$:

3
C_2
$K_1 K_2$

$\rightarrow 0$ since $C_2 = 0$

For $P_3^{\,1}(3)$:

3
C_3
$K_1 K_1 K_1$

Therefore

$$P_3^{\,1} = P_3^{\,1}(3) = cC_3(s_1, s_2, s_3) \prod_{i=1}^{3} [1 - K_1(s_i)] \tag{3.19}$$

(c) And $P_3^{\,3} = P_3^{\,3}(3) \rightarrow$

1	1	1
C_1	C_1	C_1
K_1	K_1	K_1

$$\rightarrow d \prod_{i=1}^{3} C_1(s_i)[1 - K_1(s_i)]$$

$$Q_3^{\,1} = P_3^{\,1} + P_3^{\,3}$$

$$0 = cC_3(s_1, s_2, s_3) \prod_{i=1}^{3} [1 - K_1(s_i)] + d \prod_{i=1}^{3} C_1(s_i)[1 - K_1(s_i)] \tag{3.20}$$

and we obtain

$$C_3(s_1, s_2, s_3) = -\frac{d}{c}\, C_1(s_1)\, C_1(s_2)\, C_1(s_3) \tag{3.21}$$

Similarly, for C_5,

$$0 = +cC_5(s_1, s_2, s_3, s_4, s_5) \prod_{i=1}^{5} [1 - K_1(s_i)]$$

$$+ 3\,dC_1(s_1)\, C_1(s_2)\, C_3(s_3, s_4, s_5) \prod_{i=1}^{5} [1 - K_1(s_i)] \tag{3.22}$$

which yields

$$C_5(s_1, s_2, s_3, s_4, s_5) = -\frac{3d}{c} C_1(s_1) C_1(s_2) C_3(s_3, s_4, s_5)$$

$$= +3\frac{d^2}{c^2} \prod_{i=1}^{5} C_1(s_i) \qquad (3.23)$$

For C_7,

$$0 = +cC_7(s_1, s_2, s_3, \ldots, s_7) \prod_{i=1}^{7} [1 - K_1(s_i)]$$

$$+ 3dC_1(s_1) C_1(s_2) C_5(s_3, s_4, s_5, s_6, s_7) \qquad (3.24)$$

and we obtain

$$C_7(s_1, s_2, s_3, \ldots, s_7) = -\frac{9d^3}{c^3} \prod_{i=1}^{7} C_1(s_i) \qquad (3.25)$$

In this case, we can see the form of the succeeding kernels. They consist of C_1 followed by a nonlinear no-memory element. The compensator could be synthesized as in Figure 3.3. But

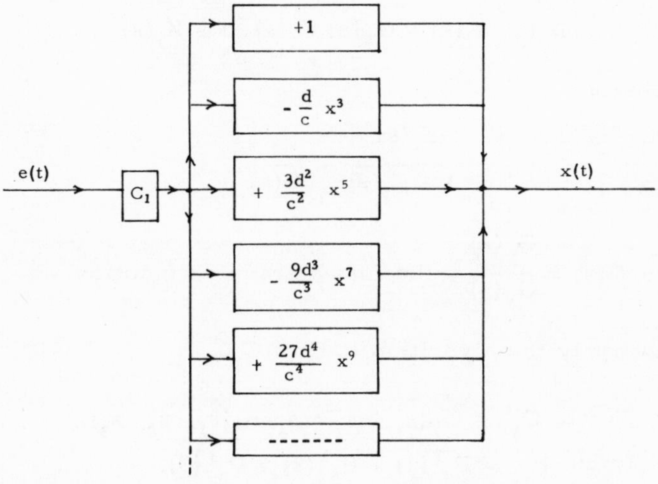

Figure 3.3. Series compensation — derived form

for $x^2 < |\frac{c}{3d}|$, the no-memory terms form a convergent power series so that the system takes the form shown in Figure 3.4.

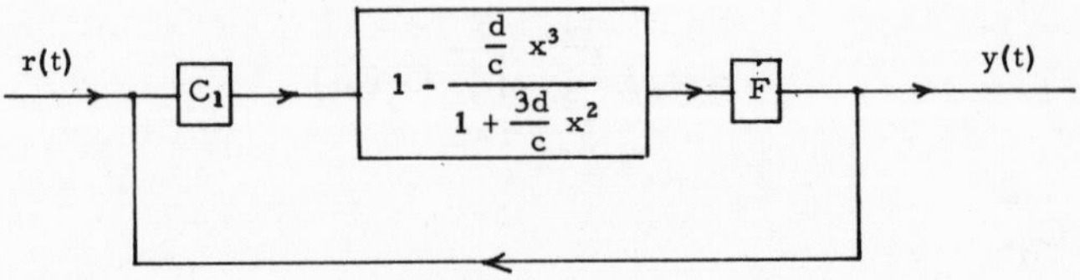

Figure 3.4. Series compensation — synthesis form

Now let us observe a system whose fixed elements are describe by the differential equation

$$L[y] = L[x] + dx^3 \tag{3.26}$$

Let the filter operation be specified as

$$y(t) = \int_{-\infty}^{\infty} K_1(t - \tau)\, r(\tau)\, d\tau$$

$$+\int_{-\infty}^{\infty}\int_{-\infty}^{\infty}\int_{-\infty}^{\infty} K_3(t - \tau_1,\ t - \tau_2,\ t - \tau_3)\, r(\tau_1)\, r(\tau_2)\, r(\tau_3)\, d\tau_1\, d\tau_2\, d\tau_3 \tag{3.27}$$

We can write the equation for the linear term by inspection:

$$G_y(s)\, K_1(s) = G_x(s)\, C_1(s)\, [1 - K_1(s)] \tag{3.28}$$

and obtain

$$C_1(s) = \frac{K_1(s)}{1 - K_1(s)} \cdot \frac{1}{G(s)} \tag{3.29}$$

where $G(s) = \frac{G_x(s)}{G_y(s)}$, the linear transfer function.

Now apply the algorithm to find C_3.

(a) First, $Q_3^1 = G_y(s_1 + s_2 + s_3)\, K_3(s_1, s_2, s_3)$.

(b) Next, $P_3^1 = P_3^1(1) + P_3^1(2) + P_3^1(3)$.

Construct partitions for the various terms:

For $P_3^{\,1}(1)$:

3
C_1
K_3

$\rightarrow -C_1(s_1 + s_2 + s_3)\, K_3(s_1, s_2, s_3)$

For $P_3^{\,1}(2)$:

3
C_2
$K_1 K_2$

$\rightarrow 0$

since $C_2 = 0$

For $P_3^{\,1}(3)$

3
C_3
$K_1 K_1 K_1$

$\rightarrow -C_3(s_1, s_2, s_3) \prod_{i=1}^{3} [1 - K_1(s_i)]$

Thus

$$P_3^{\,1} = G_x(s_1 + s_2 + s_3) \Big[-C_1(s_1 + s_2 + s_3)\, K_3(s_1, s_2, s_3) - C_3(s_1, s_2, s_3) \prod_{i=1}^{3} [1 - K_1(s_i)] \Big] \tag{3.30}$$

(c) Then

$$P_3^{\,3} = P_3^{\,3}(3) = dC_1(s_1)\, C_1(s_2)\, C_1(s_3) \prod_{i=1}^{3} [1 - K_1(s_i)]$$

We obtain

$$Q_3^{\,1} = P_3^{\,1} + P_3^{\,3}$$

or

$$G_y(s)\, K_3(s_1, s_2, s_3) = G_x(\hat{s}) \Big[-C_1(s)\, K_3(s_1, s_2, s_3) + C_3(s_1, s_2, s_3) \prod_{i=1}^{3} [1 - K_1(s_i)] + dC_1(s_1)\, C_1(s_2)\, C_1(s_3) \prod_{i=1}^{3} [1 - K_1(s_i)] \Big] \tag{3.31}$$

where $\hat{s} \equiv s_1 + s_2 + s_3$. Therefore

$$C_3(s_1, s_2, s_3) = +\frac{1}{G(\hat{s})} \cdot \frac{+K_3(s_1, s_2, s_3)}{\prod_{i=1}^{3} [1 - K_1(s_i)]}$$

$$+ C_1(\hat{s}) \frac{K_3(s_1, s_2, s_3)}{\prod_{i=1}^{3} [1 - K_1(s_i)]} - \frac{d}{G_x(\hat{s})} C_1(s_1) C_1(s_2) C_1 \quad (3.32)$$

Noting that

$$\frac{1}{G(\hat{s})} + C_1(\hat{s}) = \frac{1}{1 - K_1(\hat{s})} \cdot \frac{1}{G(\hat{s})}$$

we can see that $C_3(s_1, s_2, s_3)$ can be synthesized, as shown in Figure 3.5.

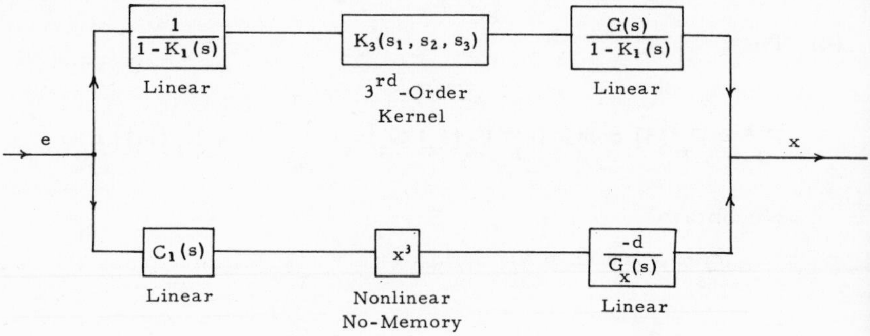

Figure 3.5. Synthesis of third-order kernel

Now apply the algorithm again to find C_5.

(a) Since $K_n = 0$ for $n > 3$, $Q_5^1 = 0$.

(b) And $P_5^1 = P_5^1(1) + P_5^1(3) + P_5^1(5)$, since $P_m^n(i)$ for odd i will always be zero in this problem. Next, construct the partitions:

For $P_5^1(1)$:

5
C_1
K_5

$\rightarrow 0$

since $K_5 = 0$

For $P_5^1(3)$:

5
C_3
$K_1 K_1 K_3$

$$K_1 K_1 K_3 \rightarrow -3\, C_3(s_1,\ s_2,\ s_3 + s_4 + s_5) \prod_{i=1}^{2} [1 - K_1(s_i)] \times K_3(s_3,\ s_4,\ s_5)$$

$$K_1 K_2 K_2 \rightarrow 0$$

For $P_5^1(5)$:

5
C_5
$K_1 \ldots K_1$

$$\rightarrow + C_5(s_1,\ s_2,\ s_3,\ s_4,\ s_5) \prod_{i=1}^{5} [1 - K_1(s_i)]$$

Therefore

$$P_5^1 = G_X(\hat{\hat{s}}) \left\{ -3C_3(s_1,\ s_2,\ s_3,\ s_4,\ s_5) \prod_{i=1}^{2} [1 - K_1(s_i)]\, K_3(s_3,\ s_4,\ s_5) + C_5(s_1,\ s_2,\ s_3,\ s_4,\ s_5) \prod_{i=1}^{5} [1 - K_1(s_i)] \right\}$$

where $$\hat{\hat{s}} = \sum_{i=1}^{5} s_i$$

(c) Then $P_5^3 = P_5^3(3) + P_5^3(5)$.

For $P_5^3(3)$:

1	1	3
C_1	C_1	C_1
K_1	K_1	K_3

$$\rightarrow -3d\, C_1(s_1)\, C_1(s_2)\, C_1(s_3 + s_4 + s_5) \prod_{i=1}^{2} [1 - K_1(s_i)] \times K_3(s_3,\ s_4,\ s_5)$$

For $P_5^3(5)$

2	1	3
C_1	C_1	C_3
K_1	K_1	K_3

$$\rightarrow -3d\, C_1(s_1)\, C_1(s_2)\, C_3(s_3,\ s_4,\ s_5) \prod_{i=1}^{5} [1 - K_1(s_i)]$$

Therefore the equation for C_5 is

$$0 = P_5^{\,1} + P_5^{\,3}$$

$$0 = G_x(\hat{\hat{s}}) \Big\{ -3\,C_3(s_1, s_2, s_3 + s_4 + s_5) \prod_{i=1}^{2} [1 - K_1(s_i)]\, K_3(s_3, s_4,$$

$$+ C_5(s_1, s_2, s_3, s_4, s_5) \prod_{i=1}^{5} [1 - K_1(s_i)] \Big\}$$

$$- 3d\,C_1(s_1)\,C_1(s_2)\,C_1(s_3 + s_4 + s_5) \prod_{i=1}^{2} [1 - K_1(s_i)]\, K_3(s_3, s_4, s$$

$$+ 3d\,C_1(s_1)\,C_1(s_2)\,C_3(s_3, s_4, s_5) \prod_{i=1}^{5} [1 - K_1(s_i)] \qquad (3.33)$$

We obtain

$$C_5(s_1, s_2, s_3, s_4, s_5) = 3\,C_3(s_1, s_2, s_3, s_4, s_5) \frac{K_3(s_3, s_4, s_5)}{\prod_{i=3}^{5} [1 - K_1(s_i)]}$$

$$+ \frac{3d}{G_x(\hat{\hat{s}})}\, C_1(s_1)\,C_1(s_2)\,C_1(s_3 + s_4 + s_5)$$

$$\times \frac{K_3(s_3, s_4, s_5)}{\prod_{i=3}^{5} [1 - K_1(s_i)]}$$

$$- \frac{3d}{G_x(\hat{\hat{s}})}\, C_1(s_1)\,C_1(s_2)\,C_3(s_3, s_4, s_5)$$

$$(3.34)$$

Synthesis of the second and third terms is shown in Figure 3.6. To synthesize the first term, we must use the idea of a generalized impulse response.[11]

The transform represents

$$\int_{-\infty}^{\infty}\int_{-\infty}^{\infty}\int_{-\infty}^{\infty} C_3(t - \tau_1, t - \tau_2, t - \tau_3)\, b(\tau_1)\, b(\tau_2)\, d(\tau_3)\, d\tau_1\, d\tau_2\, d\tau_3$$

$$(3.35)$$

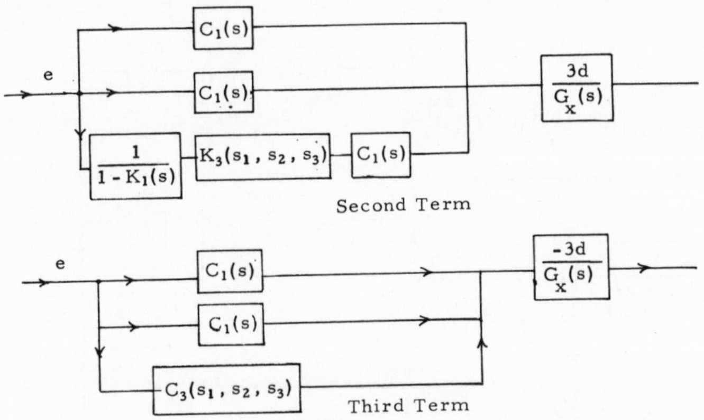

Figure 3.6. Synthesis of fifth-order kernel (second and third terms)

where

$$b(\tau_1) = e(\tau_1)$$

$$d(\tau_3) = \int_{-\infty}^{\infty}\int_{-\infty}^{\infty}\int_{-\infty}^{\infty} K'(\tau_3 - a_1, \tau_3 - a_2, \tau_3 - a_3)\, e(a_1)\, e(a_2)\, e(a_3)\, da_1\, da_2\, da_3 \tag{3.36}$$

and K'(., ., .) is the inverse transform of

$$\frac{K_3(s_1, s_2, s_3)}{\prod_{i=1}^{3} [1 - K_1(s_i)]}$$

It is impossible to realize this transform with a single system, since all of the inputs have to be the same physically.

We can see that the composite operation shown in Figure 3.7 produces the desired result. The determination and synthesis of higher-order terms follows along the same lines.

An important point to note is that each compensator is made up of combinations of three types of elements: (1) linear filters, (2) nonlinear no-memory devices, and (3) the original filter kernels. By examining the way in which the algorithm specifies the compensator kernels, we can see that the compensator kernels are always made up of combinations of these three types of elements. The significance of this becomes clear when we consider the synthesis problem.

Next, let us discuss the approximation errors in synthesis. At the present time, arbitrary kernels of order higher than 1 cannot be synthesized exactly. Thus we are forced to consider the following problem.

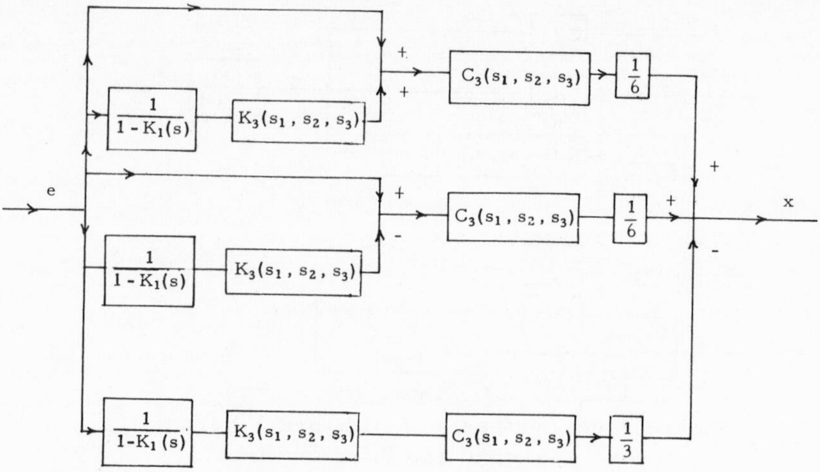

Figure 3.7. Synthesis of fifth-order kernel (first term)

Some arbitrary $K_{ND}(\tau_1, \tau_2, \ldots, \tau_n)$ is specified. For an input a(t), its output is

$$b_D(t) = \int_{-\infty}^{\infty} \cdots \int_{-\infty}^{\infty} K_{ND}(\tau_1, \tau_2, \ldots, \tau_n)\, a(t-\tau_1) \ldots a(t-\tau_n)\, d\tau_1 \ldots \tag{3.37}$$

We want to build a system $K_{NA}(\tau_1, \tau_2, \ldots, \tau_n)$ whose output for the same input a(t) is

$$b_A(t) = \int_{-\infty}^{\infty} \cdots \int_{-\infty}^{\infty} K_{NA}(\tau_1, \tau_2, \ldots, \tau_n)\, a(t-\tau_1) \ldots a(t-\tau_n)\, d\tau_1 \ldots \tag{3.38}$$

We construct K_{NA} in such a manner that $\overline{[b_D(t) - b_A(t)]^2}$ is minimized. Clearly, even to start a solution to this problem, we have to know the input statistics. Now the kernels that we wish to approximate are located physically inside the feedback loop. Since the statistics are indeterminable, any efficient type of synthesis appears difficult. We recall, however, that the only higher-order kernels which appeared in our solutions were the original optimum filter kernels. Therefore we can solve the synthesis problem indicated above with K_{nd} equal to K_n (the optimum filter kernels). We have now moved the approximation problem outside the loop.

This means that the expected value of the error from an approximate synthesis technique will be the same in the closed-loop system as in the original filter configuration.

Now let us inspect a system of the form shown in Figure 3.2.

The problem is to determine a series of kernels for C_b so that a desired filtering operation can be performed.

3. Algorithm for Determining Feedback Compensator Kernels

The equations describing the operation of the system are

$$c(t) = \int_{-\infty}^{\infty} C_1(t-\tau)\, y(\tau)\, d\tau + \int_{-\infty}^{\infty}\int_{-\infty}^{\infty} C_2(t-\tau_1, t-\tau_2)\, y(\tau_1)\, y(\tau_2)\, d\tau_1\, d\tau_2 + \ldots \tag{3.39}$$

$$P_1(x, \dot{x}, \ddot{x}, \ldots, x^{(r)}) = P_2(y, \dot{y}, \ddot{y}, \ldots, y^{(s)}) \tag{3.40}$$

$$x(t) = r(t) - c(t) \tag{3.41}$$

In addition, we want the system output to satisfy the constraint equation

$$y(t) = \int_{-\infty}^{\infty} K_1(t-\tau)\, r(\tau)\, d\tau + \int_{-\infty}^{\infty}\int_{-\infty}^{\infty} K_2(t-\tau_1, t-\tau_2)\, r(\tau_1)\, r(\tau_2)\, d\tau_1\, d\tau_2 + \ldots \tag{3.42}$$

Using the same approacn as in the series compensator case, we can write an equation of the form

$$Q_m^{\ s} + Q_m^{\ s-1} + \ldots Q_m^{\ 1} = P_m^{\ r} + P_m^{\ r-1} + \ldots P_m^{\ 1} \tag{3.43}$$

for each $m = 1, 2, \ldots$. Once again, the unknown kernel appears only in $P_m^{\ 1}$. Therefore each C_m is determined successively.

The method for determining $P_m^{\ n}$ and $Q_m^{\ n}$ will now be outlined. The techniques are similar to those in the series case.

Consider the construction of $P_m^{\ n}$, the contribution of an nth-order nonlinearity of the input to an mth-order feedback compensator kernel. As in the series case, $P_m^{\ n}$ consists of a sum of $m - n + 1$ terms, $P_m^{\ n}(i)$. The structure of the component terms $P_m^{\ n}(i)$ is identical with the series compensation terms, but the actual functions are different. The construction of $P_m^{\ n}(i)$ involves three steps. First, form all partitions of m objects into n cells. For example, the partitions for $m = 6$ and $n = 3$ are

	(I)				(II)				(III)		
	1	2	3		1	1	4		2	2	2

P_{123} $\qquad$ P_{114} $\qquad$ P_{222}

Second, examine all combinations of n compensator kernels C_j, where $\Sigma j = i$. Thus, for $i = 4$ and $n = 3$, the only set of kernels is C_1, C_1, C_2. For i = 5 and n = 3, the two possible sets are C_1, C_2, C_2 and C_1, C_1, C_3. Now compare the various sets of kernels with the partitions from step 1 for compatibility. The number of objects in any cell of a partition represents the number of variables associated with that cell. The index on a compensator kernel C_j represents the minimum number of variables necessary in its argument. Looking at partition I and the set of kernels C_1, C_1, C_2, we see that two compatible relations are

(Ia)

1	2	3
C_1	C_1	C_2

and

(Ib)

1	2	3
C_1	C_2	C_1

which could correspond to $C_1(s_1)\, C_1(s_2 + s_3)\, C_2(s_4, s_5 + s_6)$ for Ia and to $C_1(s_1)\, C_2(s_2, s_3)\, C_1(s_4 + s_5 + s_6)$ for Ib. An incorrect combination would be

1	2	3
C_2	C_1	C_1

because there is only one variable in the first cell, and the argument of C_2 requires at least two variables. If we look at the original expression, we see that each compensator kernel C_j has associated with it j filter kernels K_β. In the third step we look at the ways in which the filter kernels K_β can combine with the compensator kernels C_j, with the restrictions that $\Sigma\beta = m$ and that the total number of kernels $K_\beta = i$. Looking at partition Ia, we see that the only possible arrangements are

(Ia)

1	2	3
C_1	C_1	C_2
K_1	K_2	K_1K_2

or

1	2	3
C_1	C_1	C_2
K_1	K_2	K_2K_1

Since $C_1(s_1, s_2)$ may always be written in symmetrical form, the arrangements are identical except for ordering. Thus, except for a numerical and characteristic coefficient, we can write the term that the partition represents:

$$[1 - C_1(s_1)\, K_1(s_1)]\, [C_1(s_2 + s_3)\, K_2(s_2, s_3)]\, [C_2(s_4, s_5 + s_6)\, K_1(s_4)\, K_2(s_5, s$$

To complete $P_6^3(4)$, we repeat the same process for the remainder of p_{123} and for the other major partitions, p_{114} and p_{222}. The procedure and results can be summarized in tabular form.

$P_6^{\,3}(4)$:

$p_{123} \rightarrow$

1	2	3
C_1	C_1	C_2
K_1	K_2	K_1K_2
C_1	C_2	C_1
K_1	K_1K_1	K_3

$$\rightarrow [1 - C_1(s_1)\,K_1(s_1)]\,[C_1(s_2 + s_3)\,K_2(s_2, s_3)] \times [C_2(s_4, s_5 + s_6)\,K_1(s_4)\,K_2(s_5, s_6)]$$

$$\rightarrow [1 - C_1(s_1)\,K_1(s_1)]\,[C_2(s_2, s_3)\,K_1(s_2)\,K_1(s_3)] \times [C_1(s_4 + s_5 + s_6)\,K_3(s_4, s_5, s_6)]$$

$p_{114} \rightarrow$

1	1	4
C_1	C_1	C_2
K_1	K_1	K_2K_2
K_1	K_1	K_1K_3

$$\rightarrow [1 - C_1(s_1)\,K_1(s_1)]\,[1 - C_1(s_2)\,K_1(s_2)] \times [C_2(s_3 + s_4, s_5 + s_6)\,K_2(s_3, s_4)\,K_2(s_5, s_6)]$$

$$\rightarrow [1 - C_1(s_1)\,K_1(s_1)]\,[1 - C_1(s_2)\,K_1(s_2)] \times [C_2(s_3, s_4 + s_5 + s_6)\,K_1(s_3)\,K_3(s_4, s_5, s_6)]$$

$p_{222} \rightarrow$

2	2	2
C_1	C_1	C_2
K_2	K_2	K_1K_1

$$\rightarrow [C_1(s_1 + s_2)\,K_2(s_1, s_2)]\,[C_1(s_3 + s_4)\,K_2(s_3, s_4)] \times [C_2(s_5, s_6)\,K_1(s_5)\,K_1(s_6)]$$

As in the series compensation case, three quantities remain to be specified: the sign of each p, the numerical coefficient of each p, and the characteristic coefficient associated with each p. The value of these quantities is exactly the same as in the series case.

Next, observe the construction of $Q_m^{\,n}$, the contribution of an nth-order nonlinearity of the output to an mth-order feedback compensator kernel. The basic equation of an nth-order term is

$$[y(t)]^n = \left\{ \int_{-\infty}^{\infty} K_1(t - \tau)\, r(\tau)\, d\tau + \int_{-\infty}^{\infty}\int_{-\infty}^{\infty} K_2(t - \tau_1, t - \tau_2)\, r(\tau_1)\, r(\tau_2)\, d\tau_1\, d\tau_2 + \dots \right\}^n \qquad (3.44)$$

This is exactly the same basic equation as in the series compensator case. Therefore

$$Q_m^{\ n}\,(\text{series}) = Q_m^{\ n}\,(\text{feedback}) \tag{3.45}$$

We now have available a straightforward means of designing nonlinear compensation networks so that the closed-loop control system exhibits some specified nonlinear response. In the example given above, we were able to see the form of the nth-order kernel, and this enabled us to write a closed-form expression for the compensator. Next, let us consider the case in which a closed-form expression is unavailable, and study the effect of truncating the functional power series representing the compensator.

4. Convergence Properties

One recalls that each additional C_m that we specify enables us to satisfy the constraint equation

$$y(t) = \int_{-\infty}^{\infty} K_1(t-\tau)\, r(\tau)\, d\tau$$

$$+ \int_{-\infty}^{\infty}\int_{-\infty}^{\infty} K_2(t-\tau_1,\ t-\tau_2)\, r(\tau_1)\, r(\tau_2)\, d\tau_1\, d\tau_2 + \dots \tag{3.4}$$

to the kernel of corresponding order. For example, assume that in the set of equations 3.9–3.11, we had only used a linear compensator C_1. Then if we set $C_2(s) = 0$ in Equations 3.10 and 3.11, we have

$$K_{2\epsilon}\,(s_1 + s_2)\,[G(s_1 + s_2) + C_1(s_1 + s_2)] = 0 \tag{3.46}$$

which implies that

$$K_{2\epsilon}(s_1,\ s_2) = 0 \tag{3.47}$$

Then from Equation 3.11, we have

$$K_{3\epsilon}(s_1,\ s_2,\ s_3) = \frac{+d\prod_{i=1}^{3} C_1(s_i)\ [1 - K_1(s_i)]}{G(s_1 + s_2 + s_3) + C_1(s_1 + s_2 + s_3)} \tag{3.48}$$

Thus the linear compensator and the differential equation completely determine the higher-order kernels. In general, these will not be the same as the desired kernels in the constraint equation, Equation 3.4, so the subscript ϵ is added to denote them as error kernels.

Now consider the general case in which we terminate the compensation kernels at some finite m. The difference between the actual output y(t) and the desired output $y_D(t)$ can be written as

$$y_\epsilon(t) = \sum_{n=m+1}^{\infty} \int_{-\infty}^{\infty} \cdots \int_{-\infty}^{\infty} [-K_n(\tau_1, \tau_2, \ldots, \tau_n) + K_{n\epsilon}(\tau_1, \tau_2, \ldots, \tau_n)]$$

$$\times\, r(\tau_1) \ldots r(\tau_n)\, d\tau_1 \ldots d\tau_n \qquad (3.49)$$

where the compensators $C_i (i = 1, 2, \ldots, m)$ are used. The output $y_\epsilon(t)$ can be bounded by a simple power series

$$|y_\epsilon(t)| \leq \sum_{n=m+1}^{\infty} \left\{ \int_{-\infty}^{\infty} \cdots \int_{-\infty}^{\infty} |K_n(\tau_1, \ldots, \tau_n) - K_{n\epsilon}(\tau_1, \ldots, \tau_n)| \right.$$

$$\left. \times\, d\tau_1 \ldots d\tau_n \right\} |r(t)|^n \qquad (3.50)$$

$$= \sum_{n=m+1}^{\infty} a_{n\epsilon} |r(t)|^n \qquad (3.51)$$

where

$$a_{n\epsilon} \equiv \int_{-\infty}^{\infty} \cdots \int_{-\infty}^{\infty} |K_n(\tau_1, \ldots, \tau_n) - K_{n\epsilon}(\tau_1, \ldots, \tau_n)|\, d\tau_1 \ldots d\tau_n$$

We should like to show that there exists some M such that for $|r(t)| < M$, the series in 3.51 converges.

In practice, K_n will always terminate at some finite N. Therefore, for studying the convergence problem, we can use the series

$$|y_\epsilon'(t)| = \sum_{n=1}^{\infty} b_{n\epsilon} |x(t)|^n$$

where

$$b_{n\epsilon} = \int_{-\infty}^{\infty} \cdots \int_{-\infty}^{\infty} |K_{n\epsilon}(\tau_1, \ldots, \tau_n)|\, d\tau_1 \ldots d\tau_n \qquad (3.52)$$

since after some N, $b_{n\epsilon} \equiv a_{n\epsilon}$. Clearly, we must use the series of Equation 3.51 to actually evaluate the error bound.

We shall proceed in two directions. First, we shall show what conditions are sufficient to ensure that there does exist a nonzero M. The estimate of M that we obtain in this fashion will be, in general, too conservative. Therefore, after showing rigorously that a nonzero radius of convergence exists, we shall demonstrate a heuristic approach for obtaining a more realistic radius.

First, let us review a result due to Brilliant.[5] Consider the feedback system shown in Figure 3.8. We now introduce a more

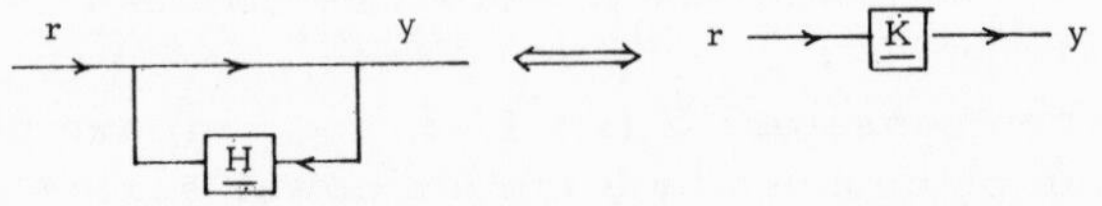

Figure 3.8. Feedback system equivalent

compact notation to represent the functional power series:

$$\underline{H}[y] = \int_{-\infty}^{\infty} H_1(\tau)\, y(t-\tau)\, d\tau + \int_{-\infty}^{\infty}\int_{-\infty}^{\infty} H_2(\tau_1, \tau_2)\, y(t-\tau_1)\, y(t-\tau_2)\, d\tau_1\, d\tau_2 + \ldots \tag{3.53}$$

and similarly,

$$y = \underline{K}[r] \equiv \int_{-\infty}^{\infty} K_1(\tau)\, r(t-\tau)\, d\tau + \int_{-\infty}^{\infty}\int_{-\infty}^{\infty} K_2(\tau_1, \tau_2)\, r(t-\tau_1)\, r(t-\tau_2)\, d\tau_1\, d\tau_2 + \ldots \tag{3.54}$$

The first step is to separate out the linear part. This separation gives the system shown in Figure 3.9a.

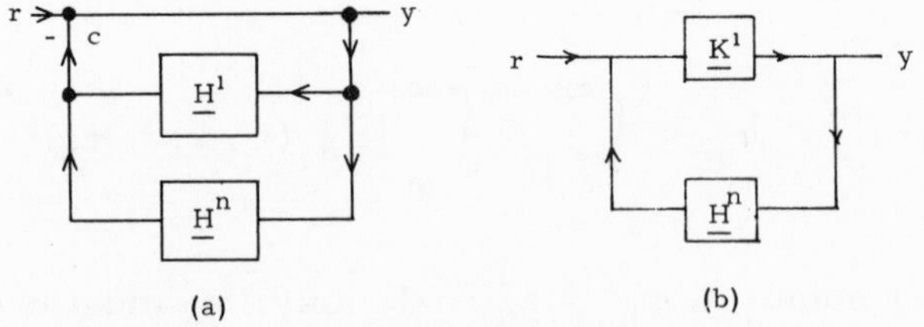

Figure 3.9. Linear separation

Here $\underline{H}^n[y]$ represents all of the nonlinear terms in $\underline{H}[y]$.

The equations describing the system are

$$r(t) - c(t) = y(t) \tag{3.55}$$

$$c(t) = \underline{H}^1[y(t)] + \underline{H}^n[y(t)] \tag{3.56}$$

Substituting Equation 3.54 and Equation 3.55 into Equation 3.56, we have

$$r - \underline{K}[r] = \underline{H}^1\left[\underline{K}[r]\right] + \underline{H}^n\left[\underline{K}[r]\right] \tag{3.57}$$

Separating $\underline{K}$, we have

$$r - \underline{K}^1[r] - \underline{K}^n[r] = \underline{H}^1\left[\underline{K}^1[r]\right] + \underline{H}^1\left[\underline{K}^n[r]\right] + \underline{H}^n\left[\underline{K}[r]\right] \tag{3.58}$$

Equating terms that are linear in r, we have the well-known linear result

$$\underline{K}^1 = \frac{1}{1 + \underline{H}^1} \tag{3.59}$$

Using this, Equation 3.58 becomes

$$\underline{K}^n[r] = -\underline{K}^1\left[\underline{H}^n\left[\underline{K}[r]\right]\right] \tag{3.60}$$

We wish to show that there exists some nonzero bound on r(t) which will ensure that y(t) is bounded.

As in Equation 3.50, we have

$$|y(t)| \leq \sum_{n=1}^{\infty} a_n |r(t)|^n \equiv B_{\underline{K}}(r) \tag{3.61}$$

Thus $B_{\underline{K}}(r)$ is a function of r and represents a bound on the magnitude of the output y(t).

Similarly, for the term on the right side of Equation 3.60, we could write

$$z(t) = -\underline{K}_1{}^1\left[\underline{H}^n[y(t)]\right] \tag{3.62}$$

and

$$|z(t)| \leq \sum_{n=1}^{\infty} c_n |y(t)|^n \equiv B_{\underline{F}}(y) = B_{\underline{F}}\left(\underline{K}(r)\right) \tag{3.63}$$

where

$$c_n = \int_{-\infty}^{\infty} \cdots \int_{-\infty}^{\infty} |K_1(\tau)\, H_n(\tau_1, \tau_2, \ldots, \tau_n)|\; d\tau,\, d\tau_1, \ldots, d\tau_n \tag{3.64}$$

From Equation 3.60, we can write

$$\underline{K}[r] = \underline{K}^1[r] + \underline{K}^n[r] = \underline{K}^1[r] - \underline{K}^1\left[\underline{H}^n\left[\underline{K}[r]\right]\right] \tag{3.65}$$

Substituting in the bound functions and using the triangle inequality, we have

$$B_{\underline{K}}(r) \leq a_1 |r| + B_{\underline{F}}\left(B_{\underline{K}}(r)\right) \tag{3.66}$$

where a_1 was defined above as

$$a_1 \equiv \int_{-\infty}^{\infty} |K_1(\tau)| \, d\tau \tag{3.67}$$

Thus

$$|r| \geq \frac{1}{a_1}\left[B_{\underline{K}}(r) - B_{\underline{F}}\left(B_{\underline{K}}(r)\right)\right] \tag{3.68}$$

The easiest solution is to plot r as a function of $B_K(r)$, and then to find the inverse graphically. Using the equality sign of Equation 3.68, we have

$$|r| = \frac{1}{a_1}\left[B_{\underline{K}}(r) - B_{\underline{F}}\left(B_{\underline{K}}(r)\right)\right] \tag{3.69}$$

Let $B_{\underline{K}}(r)$ increase from zero and plot $|r|$. The maximum of $|r|$ is equal to the bound on the radius of convergence. Since $B_{\underline{F}}(r)$ has no constant terms, there always exists an ϵ that is such that $B_{\underline{F}}(\epsilon) < 1$. The existence of a_1 is a necessary and sufficient condition for the over-all system to have a nonzero radius of convergence.

Now we must show under what conditions this result applies to our problem.

First, consider the series compensation problem. Clearly, the systems shown in Figure 3.10a and 3.10b are equivalent. In order to use the above results, we must show that the cascade of C_A, the series compensator, and F, the fixed elements, can be represented as a functional $\underline{H}$ with a nonzero radius of convergence. In addition, we require that the linear

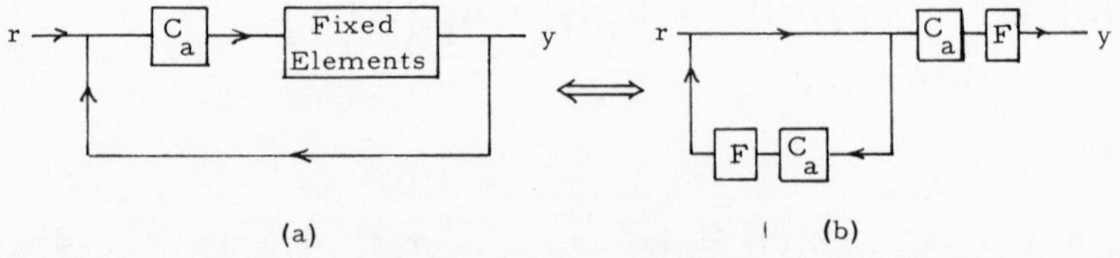

Figure 3 10. Series compensation equivalent

closed-loop kernel $\underline{K}^1$ be nonzero and stable.†

Now, in order for the cascade of two elements to be representable as a functional power series, both elements must be representable in this form. The series compensator has a finite number of terms. Therefore, if each term is bounded, C_A has an infinite radius of convergence. The functional representation of the fixed elements will have an infinite number of terms. One can show that a necessary and sufficient condition for the functional power series to have a nonzero radius of convergence is that the linearized approximation to the fixed elements be stable.

The linear approximation to the closed loop is $1 - K_1(s)$. This will be nonzero and bounded if $K_1(s)$ is stable and unequal to 1.

In the feedback case, the systems of Figures 3.11a and 3.11b are equivalent. The requirements on the cascade are the same

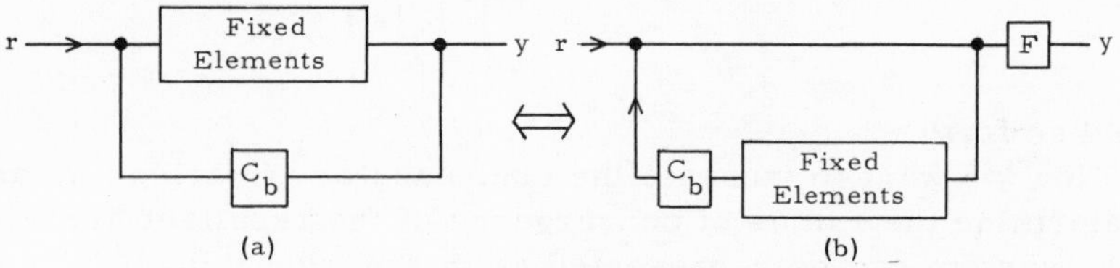

Figure 3.11. Equivalent feedback systems

as in the series case. Now we define the linearized fixed elements as having a transfer function $F_1(s)$. It follows directly that the first-order kernel of the closed loop is $[K_1(s)]/[F_1(s)]$.

This will be stable and nonzero if:

(a) The desired first-order filter kernel is stable and nonzero.

(b) The linearized approximation to the fixed elements has a minimum-phase transfer function.

Thus we have a set of conditions which guarantees a nonzero range of convergence for our compensation solution. It is clear that the bounding procedure used gives a pessimistic result. This is because we are unable to take phase shifts into account in our bound.

An example will illustrate a typical result.

Let the fixed elements be described by the linear minimum-phase transfer function

$$\frac{Y(s)}{X(s)} = \frac{G_x(s)}{G_y(s)} \equiv F(s) \tag{3.70}$$

† Here one wants to have stability even with a slight parameter variation. This requires that the fixed elements also be minimum-phase. See discussion on page 76.

Let the desired operation be described by two kernels: $K_1(s)$ and $K_3(s_1, s_2, s_3) \equiv \alpha\, K_1(s_1 + s_2 + s_3)$.

Applying the feedback algorithm, we obtain

$$C_1(s) = \frac{1}{K_1(s)} - \frac{1}{F(s)} \tag{3.71}$$

$$C_3(s_1, s_2, s_3) = \frac{-\alpha}{\prod_{i=1}^{3} K_1(s_i)} \tag{3.72}$$

$$C_5(s_1, s_2, \ldots, s_5) = \frac{+3\alpha^2}{\prod_{i=1}^{5} K_1(s_i)} \tag{3.73}$$

and so forth.

Now we want to truncate the compensator at various n and determine the radius of convergence of the resultant error series. The system can be represented as in Figure 3.12a-c.

From Equation 3.69, we have

$$|r| = \frac{B_{\underline{K}}(r) - \sum_{n=3}^{m} c_n \left(B_{\underline{K}}(r)\right)^n}{a_1} \tag{3.74}$$

We want to find r_{max} as a function of $B_{\underline{K}}(r)$ for each succeeding m. Looking at Equation 3.74, we see that it is a function of K_1. Consider a typical kernel,

$$K_1(s) = \frac{\frac{s}{100} + 1}{s + 1} \tag{3.75}$$

Then

$$a_1 = \int_{-\infty}^{\infty} |k_1(t)|\, dt = 1.01 \tag{3.76}$$

To compute the various c_n, we first find the integral of the magnitude of the impulse response corresponding to $1/[K_1(s)]$.

This calculation gives

$$\int_{-\infty}^{\infty} |k_1^{-1}(t)|\, dt = 1.00 \tag{3.77}$$

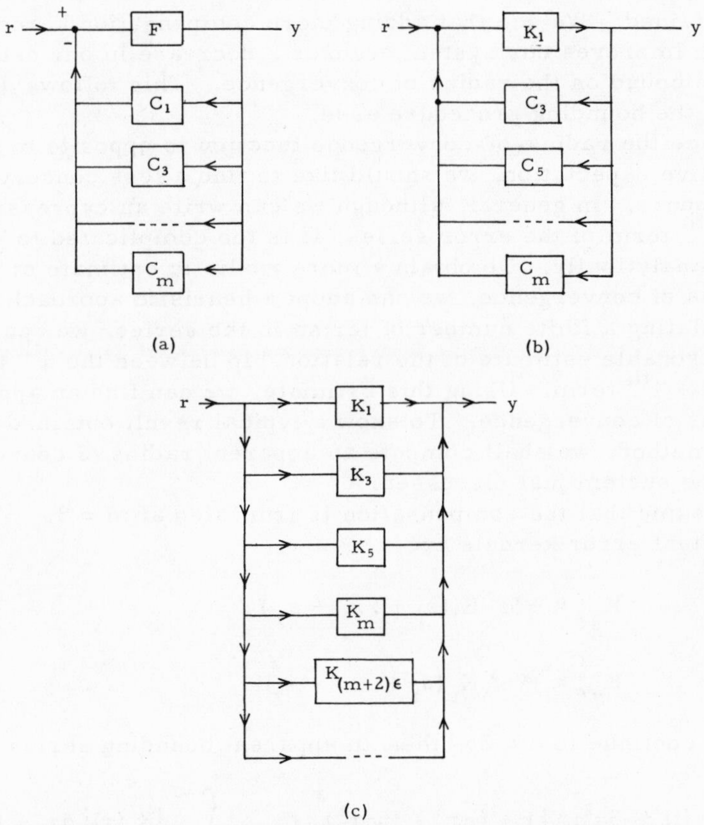

Figure 3.12. Truncated compensation system

Approximating 1.01 by 1.00, Equation 3.74 reduces to

$$|r| = B_{\underline{K}}(r) - \sum_{n=3}^{m} c_n \left(B_{\underline{K}}(r)\right)^n \tag{3.78}$$

The first four equations are

$$|r| = z - \alpha z^3 \qquad m = 3 \tag{3.79}$$

$$|r| = z - \alpha z^3 - 3\alpha^2 z^5 \qquad m = 5 \tag{3.80}$$

$$|r| = z - \alpha z^3 - 3\alpha^2 z^5 - 12\alpha^3 z^7 \qquad m = 7 \tag{3.81}$$

$$|r| = z - \alpha z^3 - 3\alpha^2 z^5 - 12\alpha^3 z^7 - 55\alpha^4 z^9 \qquad m = 9 \tag{3.82}$$

in which we have made $z = B_{\underline{K}}(x)$ to simplify notation. By performing the maximization, the function shown in Figure 3.13

is obtained. We see that adding more compensation kernels, which improves our system, causes a decrease in our estimate of the bound on the radius of convergence. This follows directly from the bounding procedure used.

Since the radius-of-convergence function is opposite to our intuitive expectation, we should like to find a less conservative procedure. In general, although we can write an expression for the nth term of the error series, it is too complicated to work with analytically. To obtain a more realistic estimate of the radius of convergence, we can adopt a heuristic approach. By calculating a finite number of terms in the series, we can obtain a reasonable estimate of the relationship between the nth term and $n + 1^{th}$ term. Using this estimate, we can find an apparent radius of convergence. To show a typical result obtained by this method, we shall compute an apparent radius of convergence for the system just discussed.

Assume that the compensation is truncated at m = 3. The resultant error kernels are

$$K_{5\epsilon} = +3a^2 K_1(s_1 + \dots + s_5) \tag{3.83}$$

$$K_{7\epsilon} = +9a^3 K_1(s_1 + \dots + s_7) \tag{3.84}$$

If we continue to n = 25, then an apparent bounding series is

$$y_\epsilon(t) \le 3a^2r^5 [1 + 6ar^2 + (6ar^2)^2 + \dots] \int_{-\infty}^{\infty} |K_1(\tau)|\, d\tau \tag{3.85}$$

This series requires that

$$|ar^2| < \frac{1}{6} \qquad \text{or} \qquad |r| < \frac{0.408}{a^{1/2}} \quad \text{for convergence.}$$

Repeating the process for n = 5, 7, and so forth, we obtain the curve shown in Figure 3.13. Thus, for n = 3, our estimate obtained by observing a finite portion of the error series is essentially the same as our rigorous bounding estimate. As n increases, the difference between the apparent bound and the rigorous bound increases. The reason for this is clear. When we observe a finite portion of the series and then extrapolate, we are taking advantage of the phase cancellations that actually exist. Using the original bounding procedure, we were incapable of doing this.

In this chapter we have demonstrated an approach that allows us to synthesize a closed-loop control system that simulates any realizable filter operation. The results always come out in a form that is suitable for synthesis. The effect of truncating

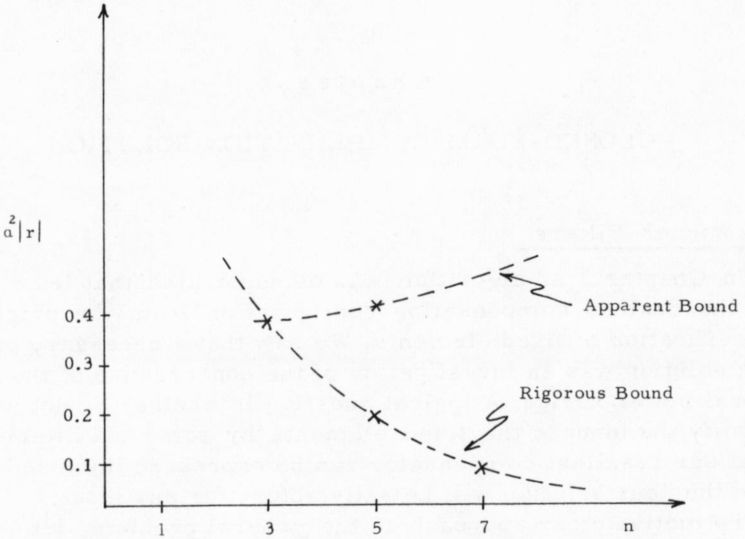

Figure 3. 13. Bound on radius of convergence

the compensation series was studied. Sufficient conditions on the fixed elements and desired operation to guarantee a finite radius of convergence were shown. The examples proved that whenever we truncate the compensation series, the input magnitude must be bounded to ensure that the actual output approximates the desired output. In Chapter 4 we shall discuss alternative compensation schemes that eliminate this problem.

Chapter 4

CLOSED-FORM COMPENSATION SOLUTION

1. Wiener Filters

In Chapter 3 an algorithm was demonstrated that led directly to the desired compensation configuration from the original specification of fixed elements. We saw that a necessary part of the solution was an investigation of the convergence of the functional power series. A logical question is whether or not we can modify the input to the fixed elements by some prefiltering so that our resultant compensator can be expressed in closed form and thus our solution will be satisfactory for any input.

To motivate our approach to the general problem, let us consider linear fixed elements. We should like to obtain the exact form of a compensator so that the final form of the control system will simulate the desired nonlinear filtering operation identically.

It is easy to show[11] that the two configurations in Figures 4.1a and 4.1b are identical. Clearly, the configuration in Figure 4.1c is also identical. Since the fixed elements are linear, the construction of their inverse is straightforward. The only problem is the synthesis of $\underline{K}^{-1}$.

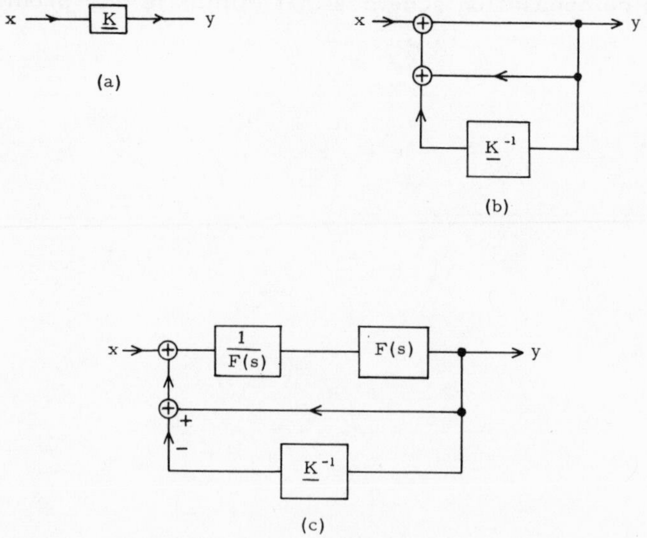

Figure 4.1. Equivalent systems

In general, $\underline{K}$ has the form of a Wiener network.† If one attempts to construct $\underline{K}^{-1}$ as another Wiener network, the problem of convergence must again be investigated. To avoid this, let us synthesize $\underline{K}^{-1}$ as a feedback system. Reasoning in a manner similar to that of an analog computer mechanization, we can see that the system shown in Figure 4.2b is the exact inverse of the system shown in Figure 4.2a.

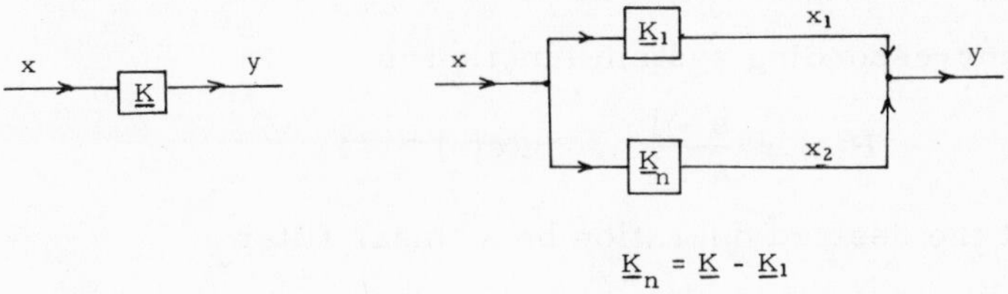

(a)

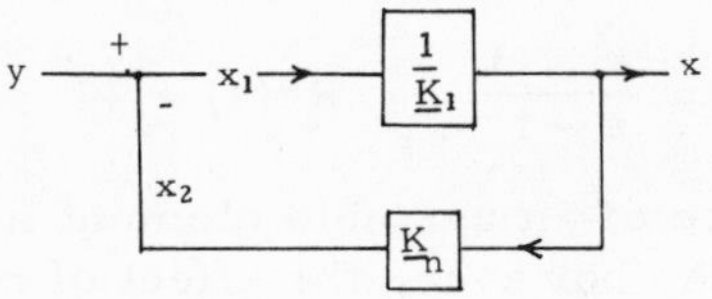

(b)

Figure 4.2. Inverse of Wiener network

By using the inverse form shown in Figure 4.2b in the block diagram of Figure 4.1b, a closed-loop system is obtained in which only the original filter components are used. Two equivalent ways of doing this are illustrated in Figures 4.3a and 4.3b. It appears to follow directly that any linear system can be compensated exactly to achieve any nonlinear Wiener filtering operation as its closed-loop response. From conventional linear control theory, however, one would suspect that this is false. The

---

† One should recall that in Chapter 2 we demonstrated the equivalence of the Volterra expansion and the Wiener characterization of a nonlinear filter. For the methods developed in Chapter 3, the Volterra representation was most useful. When one actually solves for a nonlinear filter (see references 31, 4, and 8), the resulting filter is initially in the form of a Wiener network. In this chapter, we use the nonlinear filter directly, so we refer to it as a Wiener network. Clearly, the distinction is only a semantic one.

limitations placed on the fixed elements in Chapter 3 also give an indication of this.

To point out the difficulty that arises in implementing this compensation scheme, consider a simple feedback compensation system of the form shown in Figure 3.2.

Let the fixed elements be a linear system whose impulse response is

$$h(t) = u_0(t) - 2e^{-t} \tag{4.1}$$

The corresponding system function is

$$H(s) = \frac{s-1}{s+1} \qquad \text{Re}(s) > -1 \tag{4.2}$$

Let the desired operation be a linear filter

$$K_1(s) = \frac{1}{s+2} \tag{4.3}$$

To achieve this closed-loop transfer function, the compensation must have the system function†

$$C_F(s) = \frac{s^2-3}{s-1} \qquad \text{Re}(s) > +1 \tag{4.4}$$

Now the presence of an unstable element in the loop is not necessarily bad. Note, however, the effect of moving the pole in $C_F(s)$ by a small amount. Thus

$$C_F(s) = \frac{s^2-3}{s-(1+\epsilon)} \tag{4.5}$$

The closed-loop transfer function is

$$\frac{Y(s)}{R(s)} = \frac{[s-(1+\epsilon)][s-1]}{s^3-(3+\epsilon)s+(2-\epsilon)} \tag{4.6}$$

which is clearly unstable for any nonzero ϵ. This example merely demonstrates the well-known fact that nonminimum-phase fixed elements impose a performance limitation on a control system. Another way to state this restriction is: Any fixed element with a realizable, stable inverse does not impose a performance limitation on the system. This also applies to a nonlinear system. Therefore any fixed element, linear or nonlinear, that possesses a realizable, stable inverse can be compensated, as shown in Figure 4.3, so that the closed-loop performs the same filtering operation as any Wiener network. The principal problem is a suitable test for checking the stability of the inverse of nonlinear fixed elements. This problem will be discussed in Chapter 5.

---

† One should observe that we have chosen our region of convergence so that $C_F(s)$ is realizable but unstable.

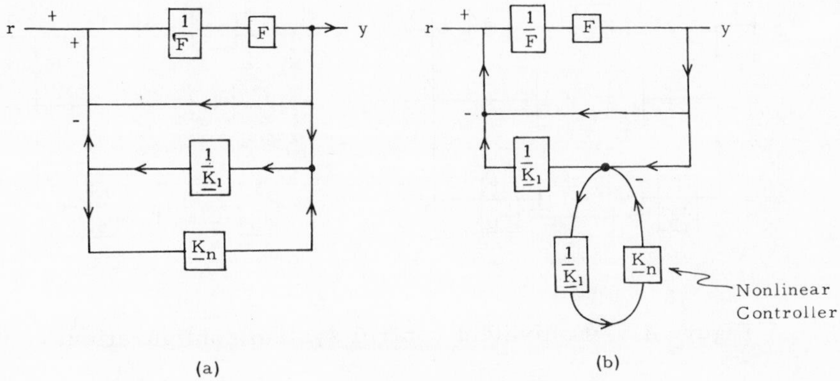

Figure 4.3. Nonlinear controller

It is important to note that the stability of $\underline{K}^{-1}$ is not required. We can have unstable elements in the loop of a continuous nonlinear system and still have a closed-loop operation that remains stable under parameter variation.

A filter of the Wiener type is capable of representing an arbitrary nonlinear system (subject to the restrictions outlined in Chapter 2). Frequently it is easier to work with a less general but simpler filter configuration. In the next section, we shall look at several simpler filters and develop an equivalent control system configuration.

2. Simple Nonlinear Filters

Notice the simple cascade filter in Figure 4.4. It can be demonstrated by block diagram manipulation that the control systems shown in Figure 4.5 are both equivalent to that in Figure 4.4. Either control system in Figure 4.5 can be generalized to an arbitrarily long cascade of linear and nonlinear no-memory elements, as shown in Figure 4.6. The only restriction on these configurations is that the nonlinear no-memory elements have inverses. The linear filter elements are arbitrary.

An example will be considered to point out the advantage of the simple nonlinear compensation schemes illustrated. Let the fixed elements be described by the linear transfer function

$$\frac{Y(s)}{X(s)} = \frac{A}{s(s + \tau_m)} \tag{4.7}$$

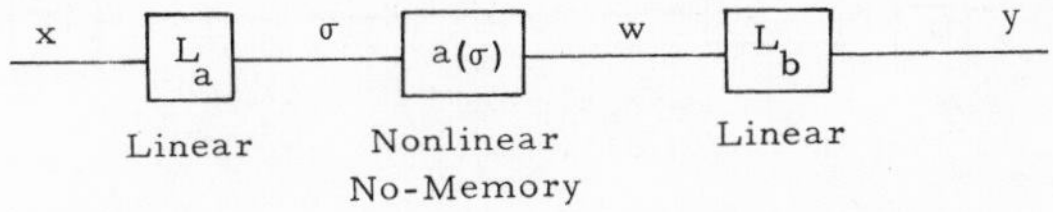

Figure 4.4. Simple cascade filter

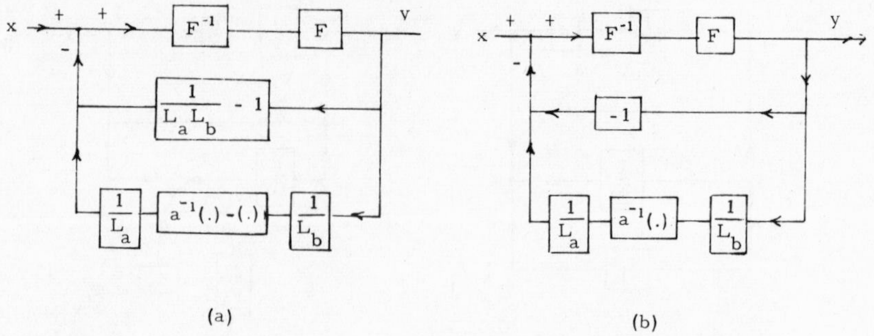

Figure 4.5. Equivalent control system configurations

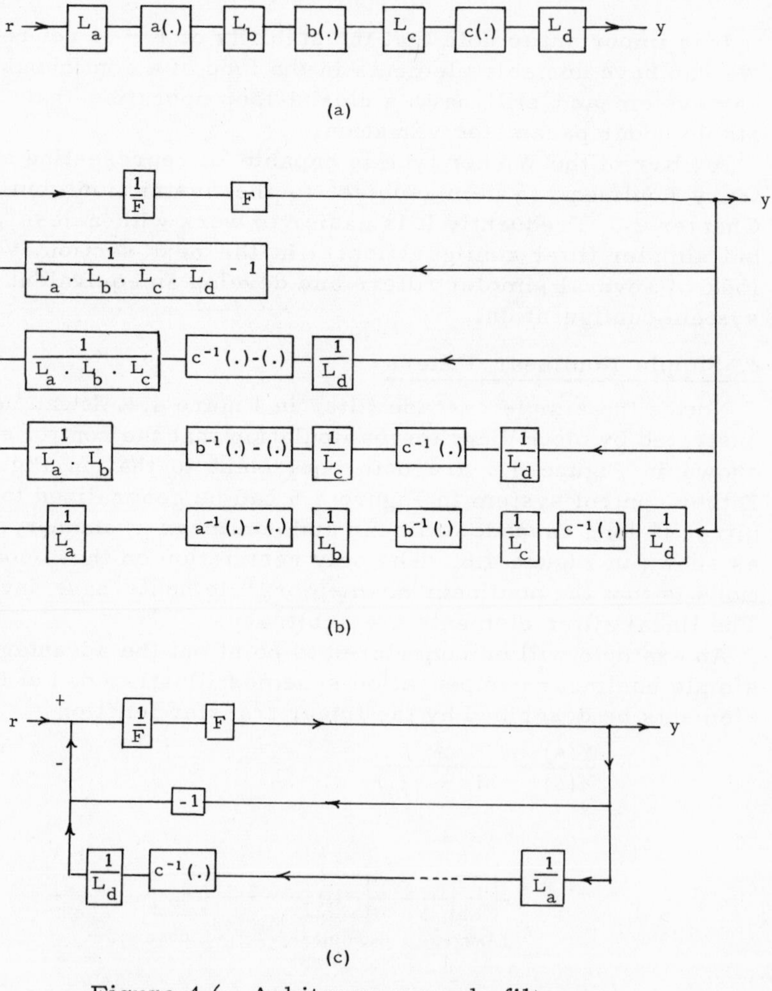

Figure 4.6. Arbitrary cascade filter

Here, in a typical case, τ_m is the time constant of the motor, and A is an adjustable gain. The input r(t) to the system consists of a signal S(t) and an additive noise N(t). We want to design a compensator so that the output of the closed-loop system will approximate S(t) in the mean-square sense.

The statistics of the input are:

(a) The noise N(t) is a sample function from a Gaussian random process with zero mean and unit variance.

(b) The Gaussian-derived signal S(t) is obtained by passing a sample function m(t) from an independent Gaussian process with zero mean and unit variance through a nonlinear function generator that is a second-order Hermite polynomial:

$$S(t) = \frac{H_2[m(t)]}{\sqrt{2}} = \frac{m^2(t) - 1}{\sqrt{2}} \tag{4.8}$$

(c) The functions S(t) and N(t) are uncorrelated. The autocorrelation functions are

$$\phi_{SS}(\tau) = \phi_{NN}(\tau) = e^{-|\tau|} \tag{4.9}$$

Since a linear filter uses only spectral information, the Wiener-Hopf technique indicates a simple attenuator, and the normalized mean-square error is equal to 1. Some form of nonlinear filtering is required. A method that is both effective and straightforward for this particular problem has been described by Lubbock.[17] Since his work is available and well written, only his results will be given here. For this example, Lubbock finds the optimum zero-memory filter and the optimum memory filter of the class shown in Figure 4.7. For the zero-memory filter, he obtains the function†

$$y = 0.0005x^5 - 0.0087x^4 + 0.0182x^3 + 0.2478x^2 + 0.4772x - 0.2246 \tag{4.10}$$

† One recalls that the optimum no-memory filter for the minimum mean-square error is simply the function $P_{s/r}(y/z)$, the conditional probability of s, given r. The probability densities of r, s, and n are available. Now

$$P_{\frac{s}{r}}\left(\frac{y}{z}\right) = \frac{P_{\frac{s}{r}}\left(\frac{z}{y}\right) P_s(y)}{P_r(z)}$$

Since the noise is additive,

$$P_{\frac{r}{s}}\left(\frac{z}{y}\right) = P_n(z - y)$$

Thus the optimum no-memory filter can be specified in terms of known functions. The rest of the problem in the no-memory case is computational.

which is shown in Figure 4.8. The resultant normalized mean-square error is equal to 0.72. For the memory filter of the class that he considers, the optimum filter is shown in Figure 4.9. In this particular case, the mean-square error is still 0.72.

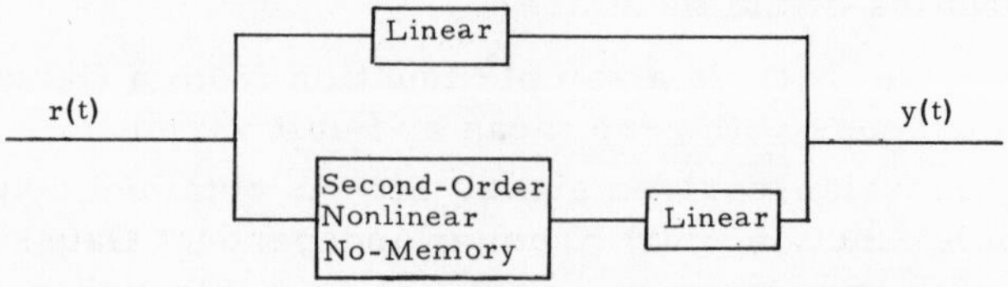

Figure 4.7. A class of nonlinear filters

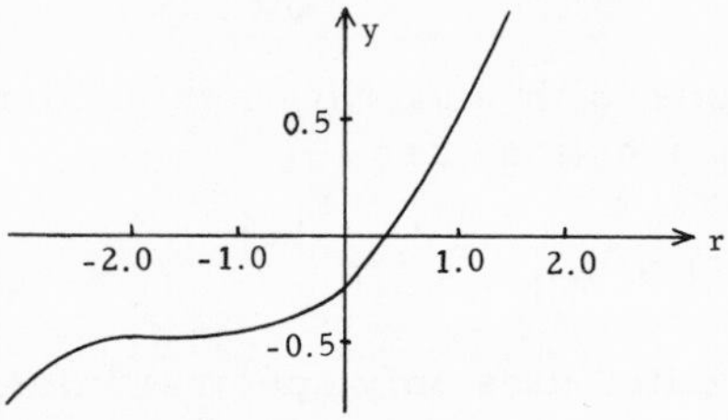

Figure 4.8. Optimum zero-memory filter

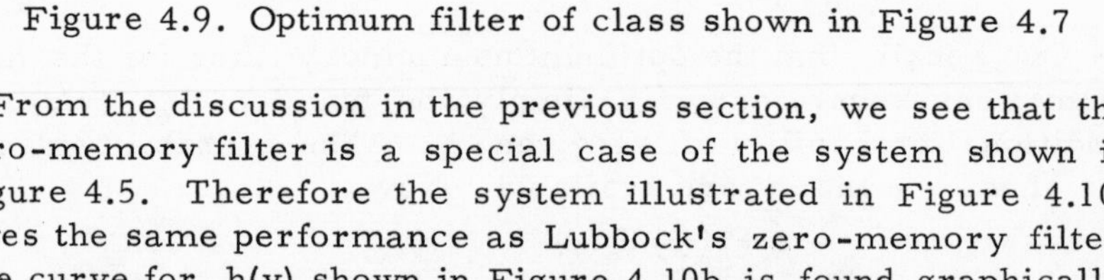

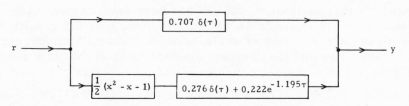

Figure 4.9. Optimum filter of class shown in Figure 4.7

From the discussion in the previous section, we see that the zero-memory filter is a special case of the system shown in Figure 4.5. Therefore the system illustrated in Figure 4.10a gives the same performance as Lubbock's zero-memory filter. The curve for h(y) shown in Figure 4.10b is found graphically.

Similarly, the filter operation in Figure 4.9 can be synthesized in closed-loop form, as in Figure 4.11.

A practically oriented control engineer might perhaps be trouble by two facets of our design. First, an ideal differentiator is present in the design. Second, it appears that a linearized model of our system has positive, unity feedback. Both criticisms can be answered easily.

The inner loop of Figure 4.11 can be replaced by the system pictured in Figure 4.12 for large A. In practice, A has only

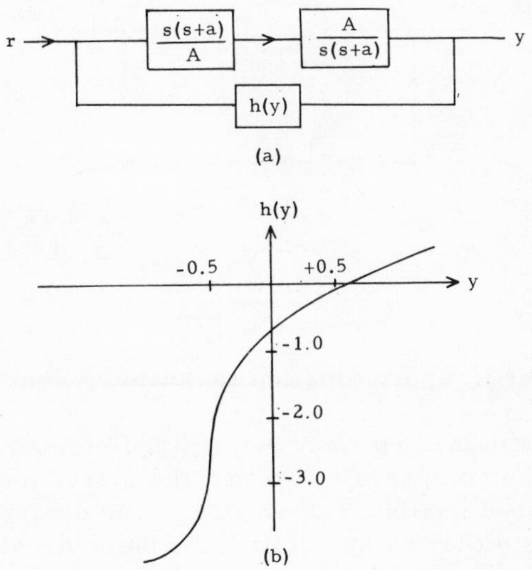

Figure 4.10. Optimum control system I

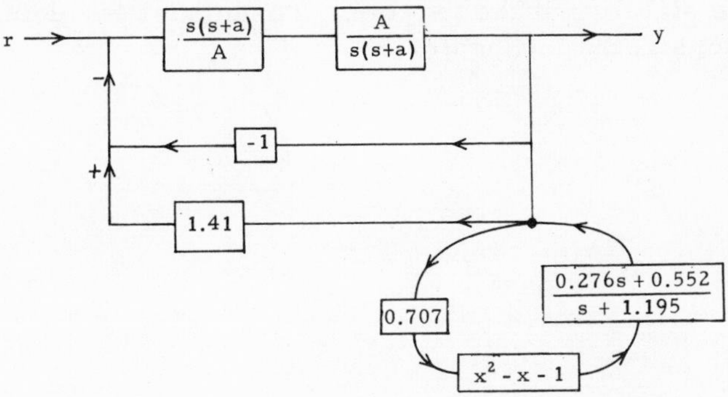

Figure 4.11. Optimum control system II

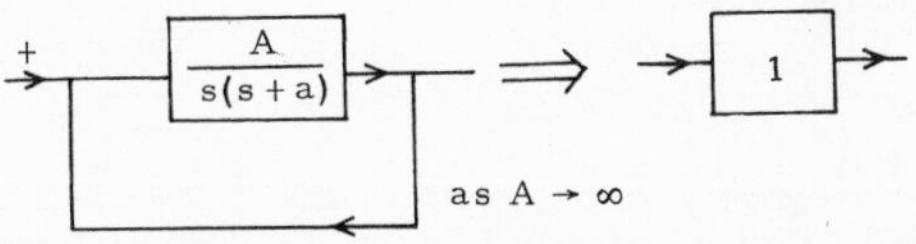

Figure 4.12. Approximation to inner loop

to be large enough so that the systems are equivalent over the particular frequency range of importance. The over-all system has the configuration shown in Figure 4.13. The nonlinear controller requires only a nonlinear potentiometer and a simple lead network as components. Actually computing the linearized model, we see that the unity feedback is only apparent. Thus our design could be implemented in practice.

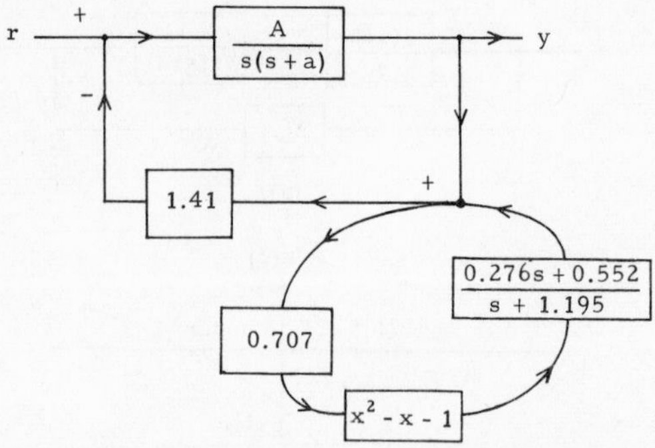

Figure 4.13. Approximation to optimum control system

We have explained how any set of fixed elements with a stable inverse can be compensated so that the closed-loop system simulates a desired nonlinear operation. The desired operation can be expressed either as an arbitrary Wiener network or as a combination of linear networks and nonlinear no-memory networks. An example showed the practical use of such a compensation scheme. To implement these techniques, we must first investigate the stability of the inverse. Techniques for doing this will be demonstrated in Chapter 5.

Chapter 5

CONTROLLABILITY OF FIXED ELEMENTS

We shall now consider the invertibility of nonlinear fixed elements. In other words, for what class of fixed elements can we precede them with a realizable stable device, as shown in Figure 5.1, such that the over-all transmission is unity?

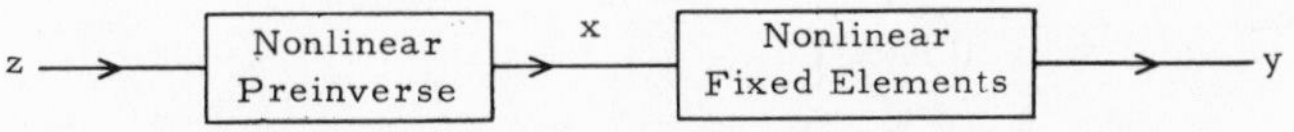

Figure 5.1. A preinverse

The work in this chapter is divided into three main parts. In the first section, we investigate fixed elements in which the stability of their preinverse is reasonably obvious. Fortunately, this class of fixed elements is fairly broad. In the second section, we consider more complicated preinverses. We discuss how Lyapunov functions can be used to investigate stability in the large of preinverses with only one equilibrium point. This section is principally expository. In the last section, we consider arbitrary nonlinear preinverses. By going from a differential equation representation to functional representation, we can employ techniques developed in earlier chapters to investigate stability.

1. Preinverses of a Nonlinear System

To illustrate the inverse problem, let us consider fixed elements described by the differential equation

$$ax^3 + bx^2\dot{x} + x = y^2 + a\ddot{y} + b\dot{y} + cy \qquad (5.1)$$

By using analog reasoning, the inverse can be constructed, as shown in Figure 5.2. We note that the subsystem to the left of

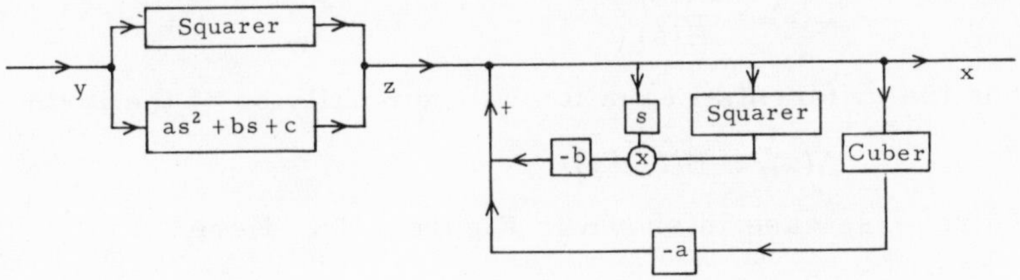

Figure 5.2. A dynamic preinverse

the intermediate variable z is necessarily stable. Thus we need only investigate the stability of the system between z and x. The most general equation that we need to investigate for stability is

$$z(t) = P(x, \dot{x}, \ddot{x}, \ldots, x^{(r)}) \tag{5.2}$$

Before looking at the general case of stable inverses, let us look at a very simple case, the separable case.†

We shall describe the fixed elements as separable if they can be represented as a cascade of linear memory devices and non-linear no-memory devices. Thus the system could be represented as in Figure 5.3a. For the simplest case (Figure 5.3b), the differential equation could be of the form

$$z = f[L(x)] \tag{5.3}$$

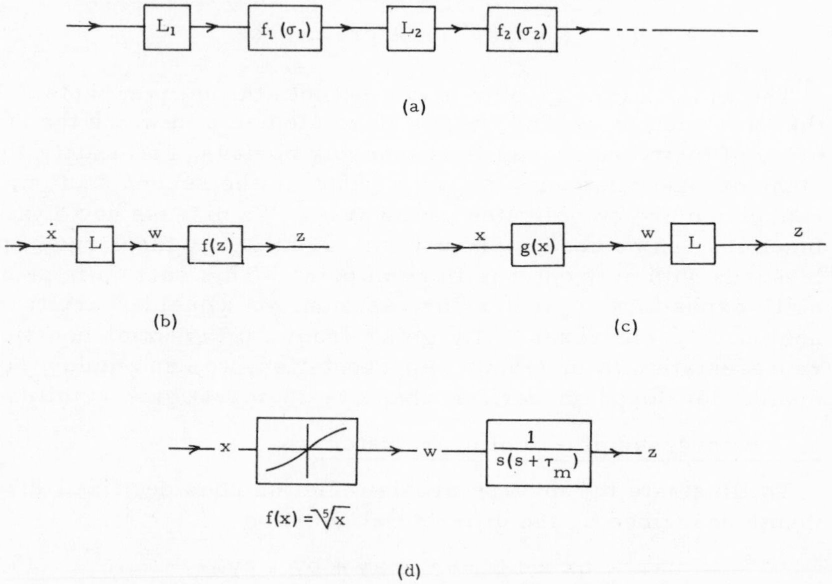

Figure 5.3. Separable fixed elements

More generally, the linear transfer function is of the type

$$L(s) = \frac{A(s)}{B(s)} \tag{5.4}$$

Thus the differential equation will normally be of the form

$$A(x) = B(f^{-1}[y]) \tag{5.5}$$

The reverse case is shown in Figure 5.3c. Here

$$A(g[x]) = B(z) \tag{5.6}$$

---

† The term "separable" as used here is not related to the "separable kernels" of Chapter 2. The distinction should be clear.

An obvious example of this case is a motor with saturation, as shown in Figure 5.3d.

The differential equation is

$$x = (\ddot{z} + \tau\dot{z})^5 \tag{5.7}$$

The longer cascades follow in similar fashion. Clearly, the inverse can be constructed by a simple cascade of the inverses of each element. The construction is possible if all of the nonlinear no-memory elements have inverses. The inverse is stable if all of the linear elements are minimum-phase. Determining the preinverse of a function of one variable is straightforward. If the mapping is one-to-one, the inverse is unique. As an example of a nonunique inverse, consider the no-memory function shown in Figure 5.4a.

It can readily be verified that the $f^{-1}(z)$ shown in Figure 5.4b is a satisfactory, although nonunique, inverse.

Consider now the system shown in Figure 5.4c. The output of the fixed elements is either +1 or -1. Thus, only $z = +1$ or

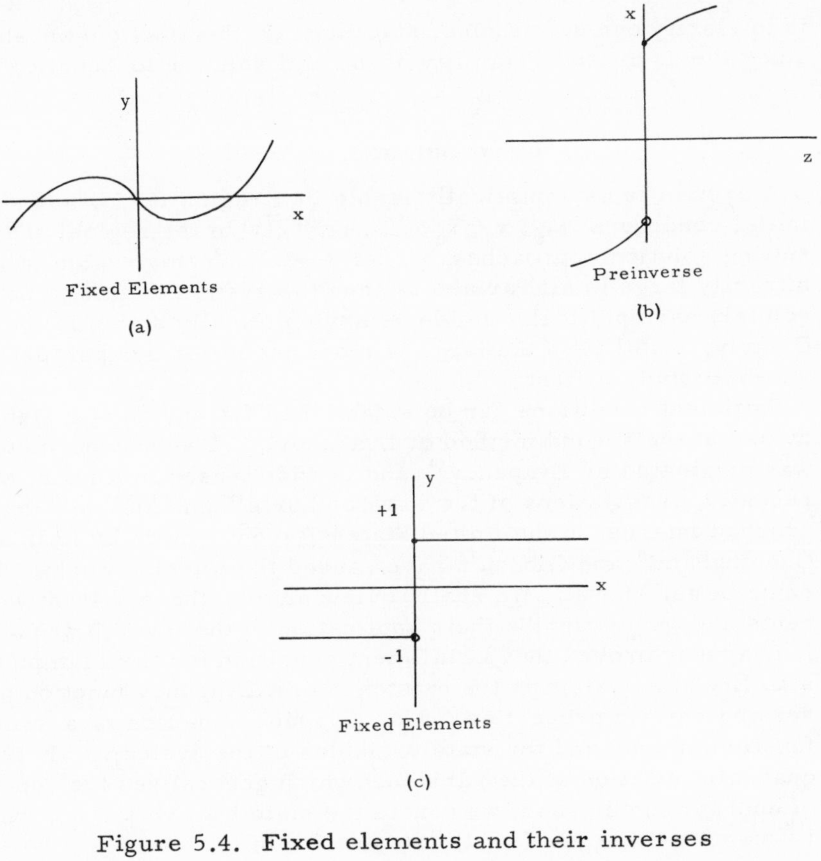

Figure 5.4. Fixed elements and their inverses

$z = -1$ could be passed through the system with unity transmission. The region $z : -1 < z < 1$ is excluded because of the discontinuity. The region $z : |z| > 1$ is excluded because of the zero slope over the two semi-infinite intervals. These are the only two conditions where the preinverse of a no-memory device does not exist.

A large number of actual fixed elements are in the separable category. We see that the construction of a stable inverse is straightforward.

A simple problem, but no longer trivial, is the differential equation

$$L[x] + x^3 = z \tag{5.8}$$

In order to investigate the stability of the inverse of this equation, we must consider a more general approach.

2. Stability in the Large of Preinverses

The first step in studying the stability of the general differential equation

$$z = P(x, \dot{x}, \ldots, x^{(r)}) \tag{5.9}$$

is to clarify our definition of stability. In this section we shall study the asymptotic stability of the null solution to Equation 5.9,

$$z = 0; \; x = \dot{x} = \ddot{x} = \ldots x^{(r)} = 0$$

$$\text{(in vector notation, } \underline{x}_{\epsilon} = 0)$$

A system is asymptotically stable in a region if, for any set of initial conditions $(x_0, \dot{x}_0, \ddot{x}_0, \ldots, x^{(n-1)})$ in the region, the resulting solution approaches $\underline{x}_{\epsilon}$ as $t \to \infty$. If this region is arbitrarily large in all variables, then the system is said to be absolutely asymptotically stable or asymptotically stable in the large. Clearly, stability in the large is most useful for our purposes, so we shall study it first.

Sufficient conditions can be established for asymptotic stability by use of the second method of Lyapunov. The second method was originated by Lyapunov[19] and is widely used in Russia. More recently, translations of the work of Lur'e[18] and Malkin[20] have aroused interest in the United States. Recent papers by Kalman,[13] Cunningham,[9] and Gibson[12] have caused the Russian work to become better known. We shall review briefly the pertinent concepts and then describe their application to the inverse problem.

Lyapunov proved that a sufficient condition for the asymptotic stability of a system is the existence of a Lyapunov function possessing certain properties. This Lyapunov function is a scalar function of time and the state variables of the system. It is a quadratic function of the variables which generalizes the concept of energy. In our case, we denote the state by a vector $\underline{x}$, whose i^{th} component is the $(i-1)^{th}$ derivative of x.

To satisfy the sufficiency, a function $V(\underline{x})$ must be found which is such that

(a) $V(\underline{x}) > 0$ for $\underline{x} \neq \underline{x}_\epsilon$ (5.10)

(b) $\frac{dV}{dt} \equiv \dot{V}(\underline{x}) < 0$ for $\underline{x} \neq \underline{x}_\epsilon$ (5.11)

(c) $V(\underline{x}) = 0$ for $\underline{x} = \underline{x}_\epsilon$ (5.12)

(d) $V(\underline{x}) \rightarrow \infty$ for $||x|| \; \underline{x}^T\underline{x} \rightarrow \infty$ (5.13)

For absolute stability, we are restricted to systems with a single equilibrium point. If there existed a second equilibrium point, say $\underline{x}'_\epsilon$, condition b could not be satisfied because $V'(\underline{x}'_\epsilon) \equiv 0$.

The stability results that we obtain for the homogeneous case will be directly applicable if we consider only inputs that are bounded in time and magnitude. In other words, if the input z(t) starts at some finite time $-T_0$ and stops at $t = 0$, we can use the state of the system at $t = 0$ for the initial conditions, and investigate the stability of the homogeneous system.

Before looking at the formal methods that are available to construct Lyapunov functions, let us cite a simple example that was given by Cunningham.[9] A passive linear circuit is shown in Figure 5.5.

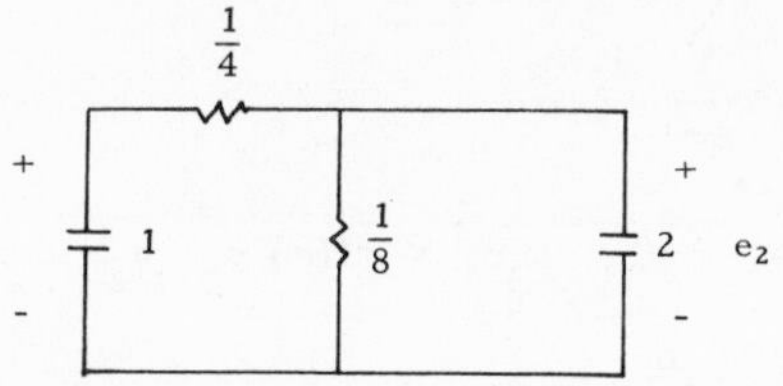

Figure 5.5. Linear circuit

The equations describing the system are

$$\dot{\underline{e}} = [A]\underline{e}\,; \qquad \text{where } \underline{A} = \begin{bmatrix} -4 & 4 \\ 2 & -6 \end{bmatrix} \tag{5.14}$$

The most obvious Lyapunov function is $W(\underline{e})$, the energy of the system,

$$W(\underline{e}) = \underline{e}^T \begin{bmatrix} \frac{1}{2} & 0 \\ 0 & 1 \end{bmatrix} \underline{e} = \tfrac{1}{2}e_1^2 + e_2^2 \tag{5.15}$$

This $W(\underline{e})$ is positive definite, so that the requirement of 5.10 is satisfied by

$$\dot{W}(\underline{e}) = -4(e_1 + e_2)^2 - 8e_2^2 \tag{5.16}$$

which is negative definite. We reach the trivial conclusion that this system is stable. In a stable linear system, the energy is always a valid Lyapunov function. Another Lyapunov function for this system is

$$V(\underline{e}) = \underline{e}^T \cdot \begin{bmatrix} 7 & 4 \\ 4 & 6 \end{bmatrix} \cdot \underline{e} \tag{5.17}$$

which satisfies all of the necessary requirements.

For nonlinear systems a more general function than energy is usually necessary. Straightforward methods for constructing this function are not yet available. Rather than examine Lyapunov functions that correspond to specific differential equations, we shall look at a method developed by Lur'e[18] for investigating certain classes of differential equations. We shall review his results briefly and show how they apply to our problem.

Two classes of differential equations are considered. (Note that these equations describe the inverse to our original system.)

Class I.

$$\dot{x}_k = \sum_{\alpha=1}^{n} b_{k\alpha} x_\alpha + h_k f(\sigma) \qquad (k = 1, \ldots, n) \tag{5.18}$$

$$\sigma = \sum_{s=1}^{n} j_s x_s \tag{5.19}$$

$$f(o) = 0, \quad c_1\sigma_1^2 < \sigma f(\sigma) < c_2\sigma_2^2 \tag{5.20}$$

Class II.

$$\dot{x}_k = \sum_{\alpha=1}^{n} b_{k\alpha} x_\alpha + n_k \xi \qquad (k = 1, \ldots, n) \tag{5.21}$$

$$\dot{\xi} = f(\sigma) \tag{5.22}$$

$$\sigma = \sum_{s=1}^{n} j_s x_s - r\dot{\xi} \tag{5.23}$$

Physically, these can be thought of as feedback systems of the form shown in Figures 5.6a and 5.6b. A typical $f(\sigma)$ is shown in Figure 5.6c. We notice that it is not necessary to specify $f(\sigma)$ exactly. We only restrict it to be a function satisfying the conditions of Equation 5.20.

The sets of Equations 5.18 - 5.20 and 5.21 - 5.23 can always be reduced to the following form by a linear transformation.[18]

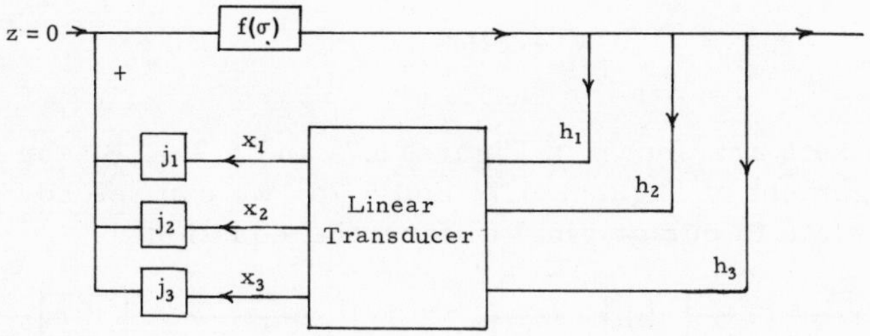

(a)

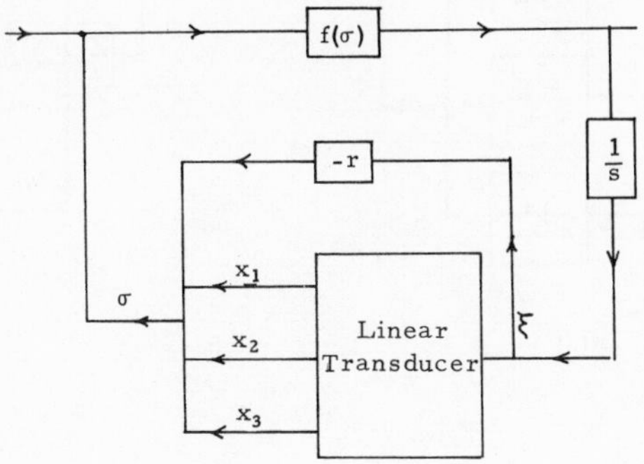

(b)

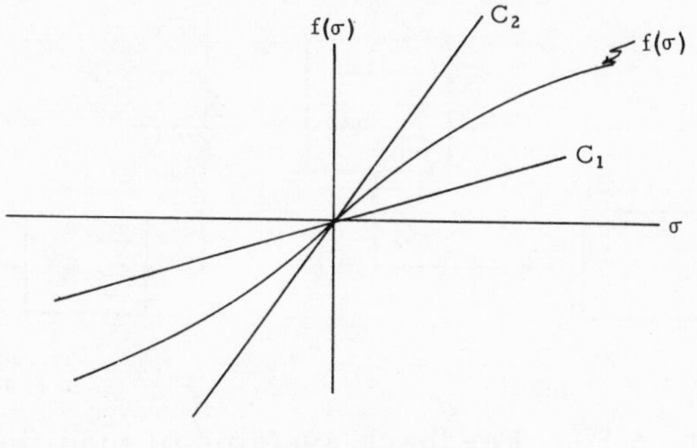

(c)

Figure 5.6. Feedback systems of Lur'e canonical form

Class I. $\dot{y}_p = \lambda_p y_p + f(\sigma) \qquad (p = 1, \ldots, n)$ (5.24)

$$\sigma = \sum_{p=1}^{n} \gamma_p y_p \qquad (5.25)$$

Class II. $\dot{y}_p = \lambda_p y_p + f(\sigma) \qquad (p = 1, \ldots, n)$ (5.26)

$$\dot{\sigma} = \sum_{p=1}^{n} \beta_p y_p - r f(\sigma) \tag{5.27}$$

These sets are shown in Figures 5.7a and 5.7b. By the simple rearrangement of Figures 5.7c and 5.7d, we can see how these two sets relate to our original differential equation.

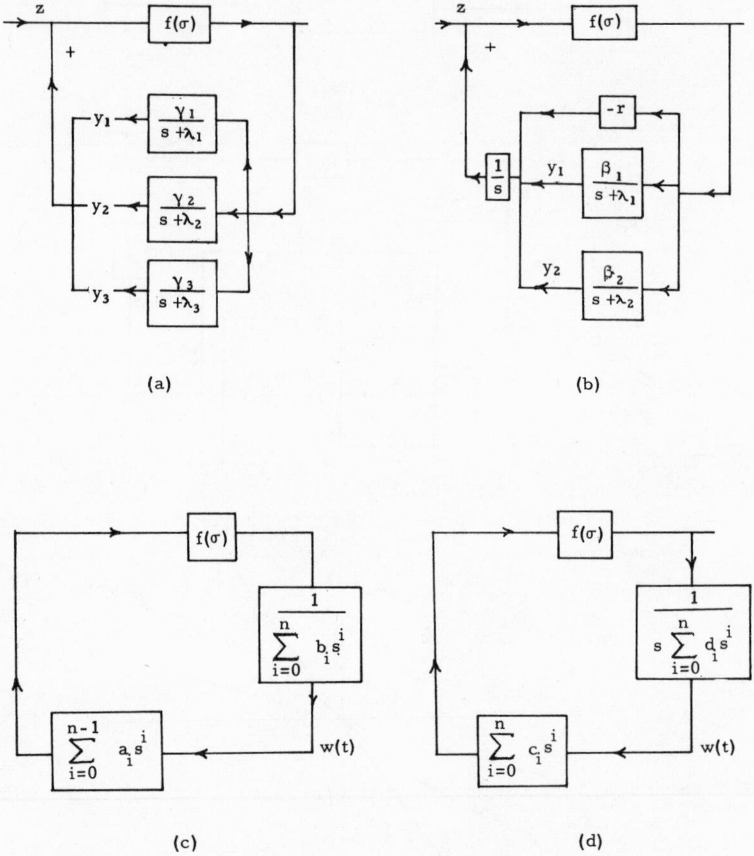

Figure 5.7. Feedback systems of modified form

The single equation describing Figure 5.7c is either

$$\sum_{i=0}^{n-1} \left[a_i s^i\right] w + f^{-1}\left[\left[\sum_{i=0}^{n} b_i s^i\right] w\right] = z \tag{5.28}$$

or

$$f\left[\left[\sum_{i=0}^{n-1} a_i s^i\right] w\right] + \left[\sum_{i=0}^{n} b_i s^i\right] w = z \tag{5.29}$$

for $z(t) = 0$, after $t = 0$.

The equation describing Figure 5.7d is

$$\left[\sum_{i=0}^{n} c_i s^i\right] w + f^{-1}\left[s\left[\sum_{i=0}^{n} b_i s^i\right] w\right] = z \qquad (5.30)$$

$$f\left[\left[\sum_{i=0}^{n} c_i s^i\right] w\right] + s\left[\sum_{i=0}^{n} b_i s^i\right] w = z \qquad (5.31)$$

for $z(t) = 0$, after $t = 0$.

Clearly, the differential equation

$$g\left[\left[\sum_{i=0}^{n} a_i s^i\right] w\right] + h\left[\left[\sum_{i=0}^{n} b_i s^i\right] w\right] = z \qquad (5.32)$$

is also included. In Equations 5.28 - 5.32, $f(\sigma)$, $f^{-1}(\sigma)$, $g(\sigma)$, and $h(\sigma)$ must be functions satisfying the restrictions of Equation 5.20, as shown in Figure 5.6c.

For the set of equations 5.18 - 5.20, a suitable Lyapunov function is

$$F = \sum_{\alpha=1}^{n} \sum_{\beta=1}^{n} \frac{a_\alpha a_\beta y_\alpha y_\beta}{\lambda_\alpha + \lambda_p} \qquad (5.33)$$

Lur'e has shown that solvability of the set of equations

$$-2a_p \sum_{\alpha=1}^{n} \frac{a_\alpha}{\lambda_\alpha + \lambda_p} + \gamma_p = 0 \qquad (5.34)$$

ensures that F satisfies the stability requirement.

For the set of equations 5.21 - 5.23, a suitable Lyapunov function is

$$F_1 = \sum_{\alpha=1}^{n} \sum_{\beta=1}^{n} \frac{a_\alpha a_\beta y_\alpha y_\beta}{\lambda_\alpha + \lambda_\beta} - \int_0^\sigma f(\sigma)\, d\sigma \qquad (5.35)$$

and the solvability of the set of equations

$$2a_p\sqrt{r} - 2a_p \sum_{\alpha=1}^{n} \frac{a_\alpha}{\lambda_\alpha + \lambda_\beta} + \beta_p = 0 \qquad (5.36)$$

ensures that F_2 satisfies the stability requirement.

Lur'e has investigated the necessary conditions for solvability of the sets of equations 5.18 - 5.20 and 5.21 - 5.23. Regions of stability in terms of the original system parameters have been developed for $n = 3$ and 4. These correspond to sufficient conditions for system stability. To establish a set of necessary conditions, we consider the function

$$f_h(\sigma) = h\sigma ; \qquad c_1 \leq h \leq c_2 \tag{5.37}$$

This gives a linear system that can be easily investigated to give a set of necessary conditions.

For $n = 2$ only,[24] the necessary conditions found in this way coincide with the sufficient conditions. Thus, for $n = 2$, a linearized stability investigation is adequate. As an example, consider the equation

$$(a\ddot{x} + b\dot{x} + cx)^3 + dx + e = z(t) \tag{5.38}$$

This is in the class of Equation 5.28, with $n = 2$,

$$f^{-1}\left[a_0 s^2 + b_0 s + c_0\right] + d_0 s + e_0 = z(t) \tag{5.39}$$

It is sufficient to investigate the roots of the polynomial

$$\left(a_0 s^2 + b_0 s + c_0\right) + h\left(d_0 s + e_0\right) = 0 \tag{5.40}$$

for all $h : 0 \leq h < \infty$ (here $c_1 = 0$ and $c_2 = \infty$).

Use of the Routh criterion gives

$$a \geq 0, \; b + hd > 0, \; c + he > 0 \tag{5.41}$$

which implies that

$$a \geq 0, \; b > 0, \; c > 0, \; d \geq 0, \; e \geq 0 \tag{5.42}$$

is necessary and sufficient for stability.

In this section we have demonstrated some of the classical techniques that are available for investigating the stability of the inverses of the fixed elements. If the inverse is not absolutely asymptotically stable, the next logical step is to try to determine asymptotic stability in a region. For homogeneous differential equations, some of the most recent work is described in a paper by LaSalle.[14] When we considered absolute stability, it was easy to relate the homogeneous and nonhomogeneous cases. For regional stability, however, it is difficult to see what conditions must be placed on the input over the finite past to guarantee that, at $t = t_0$, the "initial" conditions will lie within the stable region. An approach that gives the bound on $z(t)$ directly is the use of a functional power series.

3. Stability Investigation Using Expansion Techniques

Again study the differential equation for the inverse

$$z = P(x, \dot{x}, \ldots, x^{(r)}) \tag{5.43}$$

We write the input-output relation as a functional power series:

$$x(t) = \int_{-\infty}^{\infty} K_1(\tau)\, z(t-\tau)\, d\tau + \int_{-\infty}^{\infty}\int_{-\infty}^{\infty} K_2(\tau_1, \tau_2)\, z(t-\tau_1)\, z(t-\tau_2)\, d\tau_1\, d\tau_2 \tag{5.44}$$

As we pointed out in Chapter 3, one method of constructing this series is by use of the Q_m^n algorithm. For a differential equation of the class described by Equation 5.43, the functional power series is always infinite. Therefore we must show a region of convergence for the series. Rather than approach the problem directly, let us show how we can apply the results of Section 4 of Chapter 3 to this problem.

First, rewrite the differential equation with the linear part separated:

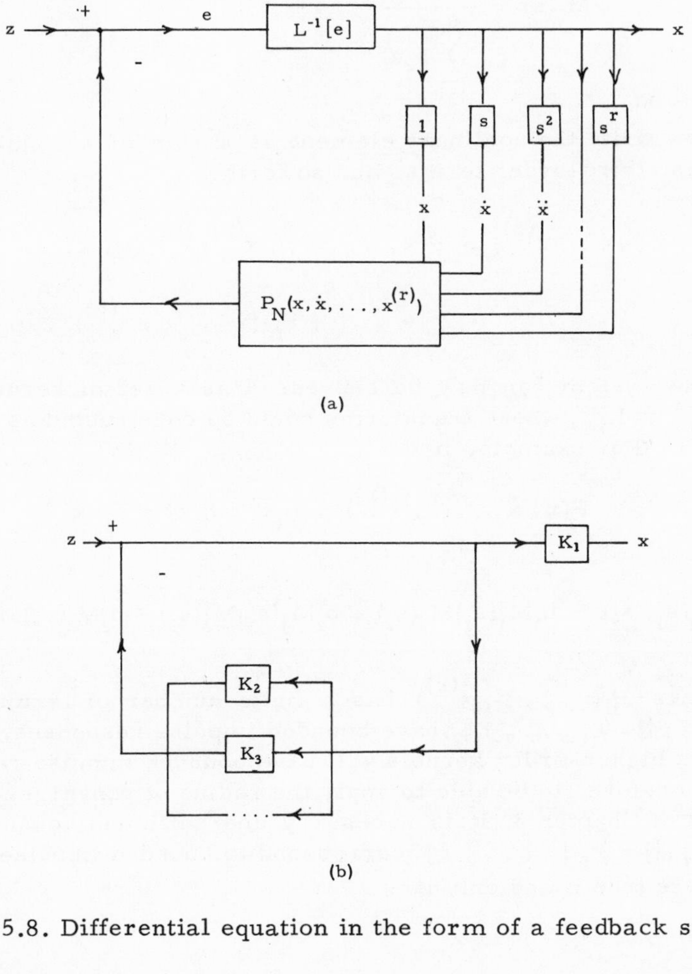

Figure 5.8. Differential equation in the form of a feedback system

$$z = L[x] + P_n(x, \dot{x}, \ldots, x^{(r)}) \tag{5.45}$$

where P_n has no linear terms. This could be represented as a feedback system, as in Figure 5.8a.

In this configuration, $L^{-1}[x]$ has a transfer function with no zeros:

$$\frac{X(s)}{E(s)} = \frac{1}{\sum_{i=0}^{n} a_i s^i} \tag{5.46}$$

The linear element can be moved forward into each path. This gives a set of linear elements which contains all of the memory in the system. The transfer functions are

$$M_j(s) = \frac{s^j}{\sum_{i=0}^{n} a_i s^i} \tag{5.47}$$

Now write the nonlinear element as a sum of second-order terms, third-order terms, and so forth:

$$P_n(x, \dot{x}, \ldots, x^{(r)}) = P_2(x, \dot{x}, \ldots, x^{(r)}) + P_3(x, \dot{x}, \ldots, x^{(r)}) + \ldots + P_m(x, \ldots, x^{(r)}) \tag{5.48}$$

The system can now be expressed as a set of kernels $K_2, \ldots, K_m$, whose transforms could be constructed as in Chapter 3. For example, if

$$P_2(x, \dot{x}, \ldots, x^{(r)}) = b_1 x^2 + b_2 x\dot{x} + b_3 \dot{x}\ddot{x} \tag{5.49}$$

then

$$K_2(s_1, s_2) = b_1 M_1(s_1) M_1(s_2) + b_2 M_1(s_1) M_2(s_2) + b_3 M_2(s_1) M_3(s_2) \tag{5.50}$$

Since $P_n(x, \ldots, x^{(r)})$ has a finite number of terms, if all $M_j(s) : \{j = 0, \ldots, r\}$ have bounded impulse responses, then all of the higher-order kernels will have bounded impulse responses.

Therefore, to be able to apply the radius of convergence argument of Chapter 3, it is necessary and sufficient to show that $M_j(s) : \{j = 0, 1, \ldots, r\}$ correspond to bounded impulse responses. This is true if and only if

(1) $r \leq n$

(2) $\sum_{i=0}^{n} a_i s^i$ has no roots in the right-half plane.

The first requirement says that if we consider $P(x, \dot{x}, \ldots, x^{(r)})$ to be a function of r variables, the linearized approximation with respect to all of the r variables must be nonzero. Physical systems will generally, but not always, satisfy this criterion. The second requirement is that the linearized approximation must be stable. This requirement for the homogeneous counterpart to Equation 5.43 is well known.[3] In the classical approach, however, we cannot determine the extent of the stability region. For the differential equations shown above, we can apply the techniques of Chapter 3 to determine a conservative bound on the region of stability. As an example, consider the differential equation

$$z = \ddot{x} + 3\dot{x} + 2x - \frac{a}{4}\left[x^2 + 2x(\dot{x})\right]^2 \tag{5.51}$$

This can be put into the form of Figure 5.8b with

$$K_2(s_1, s_2) = \frac{1}{(s_1+1)(s_1+2)} \cdot \frac{1}{(s_2+1)(s_2+2)} \cdot \frac{a}{4} \tag{5.52}$$

$$K_3(s_1, s_2, s_3) = \frac{1}{(s_1+1)(s_1+2)} \cdot \frac{s_2}{(s_2+1)(s_2+2)} \cdot \frac{s_3}{(s_3+1)(s_3+2)} \cdot \frac{a}{4} \tag{5.53}$$

The related constants are

$$\int_0^\infty \int_0^\infty \left| k_2(\tau_1, \tau_2) \right| d\tau_1 d\tau_2 = \left[\int_0^\infty \left| \tfrac{1}{2}(e^{-\tau} - e^{-2\tau}) \right| d\tau \right]^2 = \frac{a}{16} \tag{5.54}$$

and

$$\int_0^\infty \int_0^\infty \int_0^\infty \left| k_3(\tau_1, \tau_2, \tau_3) \right| d\tau_1 d\tau_2 d\tau_3 = \tfrac{1}{4} \left[\int_0^\infty \left| -e^{-\tau} + 2e^{-2\tau} \right| d\tau \right]^2 = \frac{a}{16} \tag{5.55}$$

Therefore, writing Equation 3.66 with the dummy variable y, we have

$$z = y - \frac{a}{16}[y^2 + y^3] \tag{5.56}$$

Maximizing z as a function of y gives the desired bound on the region of convergence. A plot of $|z|_{max}$ against a is shown in Figure 5.9.

In this case, we are able to determine a nontrivial region of convergence for moderate values of α. By contrast, it is not immediately obvious how to find a suitable Lyapunov function.

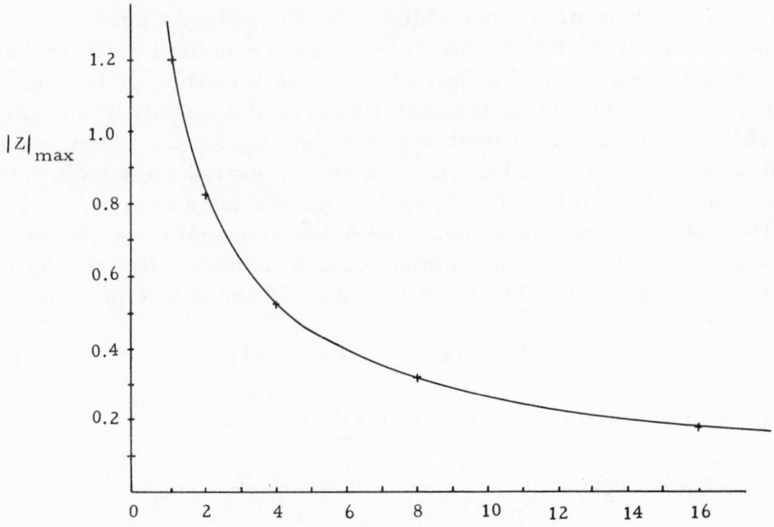

Figure 5.9. Region of stability as a function of nonlinearity

It is important to notice that the region of convergence is a bound on the magnitude of the error signal, and not on the input signal.

We have demonstrated methods of testing inverses of fixed elements. We have seen that fixed elements may be divided into three classes. For separable cases, determination of the stability of the inverse is straightforward. Next, we have looked at systems with one equilibrium point. Sufficient conditions for absolute asymptotic stability have been described. In practice, actual implementation of these tests for sufficient conditions is sometimes difficult. The third case considered was that of fixed elements whose inverse was asymptotically stable within a certain region of error-signal magnitude. Once we have determined stability of the inverse in some sense, we are assured that we can achieve any realizable filtering operation for some range of the input signal.

Chapter 6

CRITIQUE AND EXTENSIONS

In this book we have developed an approach to the problem of nonlinear control system synthesis. The approach was based on the philosophy that a control system is essentially a signal-processing system with additional constraints. Therefore, in the case of any particular feedback system, we must decide whether this philosophy is valid.

In the case where the signal input of interest to the system is a member function from a stationary random process and has been corrupted with noise, this viewpoint will, in general, be valid. Of course, there are other cases in which the dynamic response of the system to abrupt changes is the important consideration.

Once we adopt the signal-processing viewpoint, the fixed elements can be viewed as a possible constraint. There exists a large class of fixed elements which impose no constraint on the system. In the linear case, this class consists of all minimum-phase elements. In the nonlinear case, we require that the inverse of the fixed elements be stable for some range of inputs. For all fixed elements of this class, an optimum compensation scheme removes the effect of the fixed elements and creates a new system with the desired input-output relation. We have developed several methods of synthesizing this new system.

Now let us consider some of the problems involved and related areas of interest.

(a) The problem of compensating fixed elements whose inverse is unstable for all inputs is not covered. In general, the resulting mean-square error will be higher. The form of the optimum nonlinear compensation is not obvious.

(b) In the case of systems with abrupt nonlinearities (such as a "hard" limiter), the polynomial approximation will require a large number of terms.

(c) In Chapter 2, we formed part of a foundation for the synthesis of nonlinear kernels. Clearly, these results are not limited to control systems. At present, an efficient synthesis technique does not exist. The only general synthesis techniques use orthogonal linear memory networks cascaded with nonlinear no-memory elements. In this approach, one has to choose judiciously the linear networks to minimize the number. For second-order kernels and

Gaussian inputs the kernels may be specified as the eigenfunctions of an integral equation.[8] For higher-order kernels or non-Gaussian inputs the choice is not obvious.

We have seen that synthesis from the differential equation form is straightforward. Thus a general technique for going from an arbitrary kernel to a simple differential equation representation is needed.

(d) A result that is particularly useful in other applications is the algorithm that enables us to go from the differential equation characterization to the functional power series representation. This enables us to find an explicit input-output relation. Previously one had to consider either force-free systems or reasonably simple inputs. The functional representation is suitable for random, periodic, or transient inputs.

(e) The most troublesome problem in applying the functional representation to closed-loop systems is the determination of a valid radius of convergence. Our general technique was inherently conservative. In many cases, the actual radius of convergence is much larger.

In this research we have shown the advantages of a functional representation in the control system synthesis problem. By relating it to the differential equation method of characterization, we have obtained a better understanding of both techniques.

REFERENCES

1. Andronow, A. A., and C. E. Chaiken, Theory of Oscillations, Princeton University Press, Princeton, N.J. (1949).
2. Barrett, J. F., The Use of Functionals in the Analysis of Nonlinear Physical Systems, Statistical Advisory Unit, Report No. 1/57, Ministry of Supply, Great Britain (1957).
3. Bellman, R. E., Stability Theory of Differential Equations, McGraw-Hill Book Co., New York (1953).
4. Bose, A. G., A Theory of Nonlinear Systems, Technical Report 309, Research Laboratory of Electronics, M.I.T. (May 15, 1956).
5. Brilliant, M. B., Theory of the Analysis of Nonlinear Systems, Technical Report 345, Research Laboratory of Electronics, M.I.T. (Mar. 3, 1958).
6. Brown, G. S., and D. P. Campbell, Principles of Servomechanisms: Dynamics and Synthesis of Closed-Loop Control Systems, John Wiley & Sons, New York (1948).
7. Cameron, R. H., and W. T. Martin, "The Orthogonal Development of Nonlinear Functionals in Series of Fourier-Hermite Functionals," Annals of Mathematics, 48, 2, 385-389 (April 1947).
8. Chesler, D. A., Nonlinear Systems with Gaussian Inputs, Technical Report 366, Research Laboratory of Electronics, M.I.T. (Feb. 15, 1960).
9. Cunningham, W. J., "An Introduction to Lyapunov's Second Method," paper presented at the AIEE Workshop on Lyapunov's Second Method, Cambridge, Mass., Sept. 6-7, 1960.
10. Fréchet, M., "Sur les fonctionnelles continues," Ann. de l'École Normale sup., 3rd Ser., Vol. 27 (1910).
11. George, D. A., Continuous Nonlinear Systems, Technical Report 355, Research Laboratory of Electronics, M.I.T. (July 22, 1959).
12. Gibson, J. E., and Z. V. Rekasuis, "Application of Lyapunov's Second Method to Control Systems with Nonlinear Gain," paper presented at the AIEE Workshop on Lyapunov's Second Method, Cambridge, Mass., Sept. 6-7, 1960.

13. Kalman, R. E., and J. E. Bertram, "Control System Analysis and Design Via the 'Second Method' of Lyapunov: I Continuous-Time Systems," Trans. ASME, 82 (Ser. D, Journal of Basic Engineering), 371-393 (1960).

14. LaSalle, J. P., "Some Extensions of Liapunov's Second Method," IRE Trans., Professional Group on Circuit Theory, CT-7, 4, 520-527 (Dec. 1960).

15. Lee, Y. W., Statistical Theory of Communication, John Wiley & Sons, New York (1960).

16. Leimanis, E., and N. Minorsky, Dynamics and Nonlinear Mechanics, John Wiley & Sons, New York (1958).

17. Lubbock, J. K., The Optimization of a Class of Nonlinear Filters, Monograph No. 344B, Institution of Electrical Engineers, London (Nov. 1959).

18. Lur'e, A. I., Some Nonlinear Problems in the Theory of Automatic Control, Her Majesty's Stationery Office, London (1957).

19. Lyapunov, A. M. (Liapounoff, M. A.), Problème général de la stabilité du mouvement, Annals of Mathematical Studies No. 17, Princeton University Press, Princeton, N.J. (1947).

20. Malkin, I. G., Theory of the Stability of Motions, Gostekhizdat, Moscow (1952); English translation, Office of Technical Services, Washington, D. C.

21. Mason, S. J., and H. J. Zimmermann, Electronic Circuits, Signals, and Systems, John Wiley & Sons, New York (1960).

22. Minorsky, N., Introduction to Nonlinear Mechanics, J. W. Edwards, Ann Arbor, Mich. (1947).

23. Nemytskii, V. V., and V. V. Stepanov, Qualitative Theory of Differential Equations, Princeton University Press, Princeton, N. J. (1960).

24. Popov, V. M., "Relaxing the Sufficiency Conditions for Absolute Stability," Automation and Remote Control, 19, 1, 1-7 (Jan. 1958).

25. Siebert, W. M., Chapter 3 in Lectures on Communication System Theory, ed. by E. J. Baghdady, McGraw-Hill Book Co., New York (1961).

26. Smets, H. B., "Analysis and Synthesis of Nonlinear Systems," IRE Trans., Professional Group on Circuit Theory, CT-7, 4, 459-469 (Dec. 1960).

27. Smets, H. B., "Étude des Methodes d'Analyse des Systèmes Physiques Non-linéaires," travail de fin d'études aux Laboratoires des Applications de l'Electricité de l'Université Libre de Bruxelles, Brussels, Belgium (1956).

28. Truxal, J. G., Automatic Feedback Control System Synthesis, McGraw-Hill Book Co., New York (1955).

29. Volterra, V., Theory of Functionals and of Integral and Integro-Differential Equations, Dover Publications, New York (1959).

30. Wiener, N., Extrapolation, Interpolation, and Smoothing of Stationary Time Series, The Technology Press of M.I.T., Cambridge, Mass., and John Wiley & Sons, New York (1949).

31. Wiener, N., Nonlinear Problems in Random Theory, The Technology Press of M.I.T., Cambridge, Mass., and John Wiley & Sons, New York (1958).

32. Youla, D. C., "The Use of the Method of Maximum Likelihood in Estimating Continuous-Modulated Intelligence Which Has Been Corrupted by Noise," IRE Trans., Professional Group on Information Theory, PGIT-3, 1, 90-105 (Mar. 1954).

INDEX